250

PRENTICE-HALL FOUNDATIONS OF MODERN BIOLOGY SERIES

William D. McElroy and Carl P. Swanson, Editors

NEW VOLUME

Chemical Background for the Biological Sciences, Emil H. White

SECOND EDITIONS

The Cell, Carl P. Swanson

Cell Physiology and Biochemistry, William D. McElroy

Heredity, David M. Bonner and Stanley E. Mills

Adaptation, Bruce Wallace and Adrian M. Srb

Growth and Development, Maurice Sussman

Animal Physiology, Knut Schmidt-Nielsen

Animal Diversity, Earl D. Hanson

Animal Behavior, V. G. Dethier and Eliot Stellar

The Life of the Green Plant, Arthur W. Galston

The Plant Kingdom, Harold C. Bold

Man in Nature, Marston Bates

V. G. DETHIER   *University of Pennsylvania*

ELIOT STELLAR   *University of Pennsylvania*

Englewood Cliffs, N. J.   **PRENTICE-HALL, INC.**

Animal Behavior

ITS EVOLUTIONARY AND NEUROLOGICAL BASIS

SECOND EDITION

FOUNDATIONS OF MODERN BIOLOGY SERIES

ANIMAL BEHAVIOR: Its Evolutionary and Neurological Basis, SECOND EDITION

V. G. Dethier and Eliot Stellar

FOUNDATIONS OF MODERN BIOLOGY SERIES

William D. McElroy and Carl P. Swanson, Editors

Design by Walter Behnke

Drawings by Felix Cooper

PRENTICE-HALL INTERNATIONAL, INC., *London*

PRENTICE-HALL OF AUSTRALIA, PTY., LTD., *Sydney*

PRENTICE-HALL OF CANADA, LTD., *Toronto*

PRENTICE-HALL OF INDIA PVT. LTD., *New Delhi*

PRENTICE-HALL OF JAPAN, INC., *Tokyo*

PRENTICE-HALL DE MEXICO, S. A., *Mexico City*

C-03742(p)   *C-03743(c)*

Foundations
of Modern Biology
Series

PREFACE TO THE FIRST EDITION

The science of biology today is *not* the same science of fifty, twenty-five, or even ten years ago. Today's accelerated pace of research, aided by new instruments, techniques, and points of view, imparts to biology a rapidly changing character as discoveries pile one on top of the other. All of us are aware, however, that each new and important discovery is not just a mere addition to our knowledge; it also throws our established beliefs into question, and forces us constantly to reappraise and often to reshape the foundations upon which biology rests. An adequate presentation of the dynamic state of modern biology is, therefore, a formidable task and a challenge worthy of our best teachers.

The authors of this series believe that a new approach to the organization of the subject matter of biology is urgently needed to meet this challenge, an approach that introduces the student to biology as a growing, active science, and that also *permits each teacher of biology to determine the level and structure of his own course*. A single textbook cannot provide such flexibility, and it is the authors' strong conviction that these student needs and teacher prerogatives can best be met by a series of short, inexpensive, well-written, and well-illustrated books so planned as to encompass those areas of study central to an understanding of the content, state, and direction of modern biology. The FOUNDATIONS OF MODERN BIOLOGY SERIES represents the translation of these ideas into print, with each volume being complete in itself yet at the same time serving as an integral part of the series as a whole.

PREFACE TO THE SECOND EDITION

The first edition of the FOUNDATIONS OF MODERN BIOLOGY SERIES represented a marked departure from the traditions of textbook writing. The enthusiastic acceptance of the Series by teachers of biology, here and abroad, has been most heartening, and confirms our belief that there was a long-felt need for flexible teaching units based on current views and concepts. The second edition of all volumes in the Series retains the earlier flexibility, eliminates certain unnecessary overlaps of content, introduces new and relevant information, and provides more meaningful illustrative material.

The Series has also been strengthened by the inclusion of a new volume, *Chemical Background for the Biological Sciences* by Dr. Emil White. The dependence of modern biology on a sound foundation in physics and chemistry is obvious; this volume is designed to provide the necessary background in these areas.

In preparing the second edition of the Series, the authors and editors gratefully acknowledge the many constructive criticisms that have been made by hundreds of teaching biologists. Their interest and aid have made the task of writing more a pleasure than a burden.

Contents

vii

ANIMAL BEHAVIOR

Introduction

No animal lives alone. Each comes into contact with other animals sometime in its life. That most solitary of creatures, the albatross, which spends the greater part of its life at sea far out of sight of land, returns periodically to the company of its own to breed. Even animals whose reproductive needs can be satisfied in solitude—the ameba that divides by fission, the budding *Hydra,* the hermaphroditic snail, the partheno-genetic aphid—even these are not alone. They have contact with the organisms that constitute their food and the parasites and predators that prey upon them.

Thus, few animals are solitary. Many are drawn together in fluid temporary associations by shifting conditions of the environment such as the lee of a stone in a running brook, a rotting log in the jungle, a water hole in the desert, a carcass in the veld. Some are gathered in more unified communities, as shoals of fishes and flocks of birds; some live in highly integrated colonies, as ants and honeybees; others are so intimately associated, as the corals, that it is impossible to tell the individual from the colony.

Regardless of the closeness with which animals associate,

their relations are vastly different from aggregations of nonliving entities such as molecules. Although the movements of a flock of starlings or a crowd of ants on a broken ant hill can perhaps be analyzed in the same mathematical terms as are applied to Brownian molecular movement, the two are fundamentally different, and the difference is not merely a matter of complexity. The actions of animals are directed toward keeping the animals alive and enabling them to reproduce. Thus, the continued existence of an organism and of a species depends on the effectiveness of actions of the individual. This is not true of molecules. The directive action of organisms with respect to one another is one aspect of behavior.

Survival also depends on the maintenance of suitable relations with the nonliving environment. The sparrow fluffs its feathers when cold, the locust orients its body toward the sun when it is hot, the bat hibernates during winter, the swallow flies south. This adaptive relation between an organism and its environment is also behavior.

The assertion that an organism maintains relations with its environment, whether nonliving or living, implies that an organism changes in response to changes in the environment. These changes, which we call behavior, are not passive; they are directed actions, that is, actions promoting survival, and they are reversible. When an oak tree bends and thrashes in the wind, it is a passive thing. When a parasitic plant such as the dodder reaches out and twines itself around another plant, it does so by growth movements that are irreversible. By contrast, the behavior of animals is both active and reversible.

The capacity to respond to stimuli is termed *irritability* and is an essential property of living matter. Responses that do not jeopardize survival are preserved in the course of time; others are lost. In the long developmental history of animals, as cells became associated into tissues, tissues into organs, and organs into organisms, the suitability of the changes that took place in each individual cell, tissue, or organ began to be measured, not solely in terms of the individual unit, but in terms of the survival requirements of the whole. The cell that responded unsuitably was eliminated, as was also the deficient tissue or organ. In short, the course of the evolution of responsiveness has been shaped by the requirements of the whole individual, acting in his environment. Since no animal can ever free itself completely from its heredity, its behavior is inevitably coupled to its evolutionary history.

The change from a unicellular plan of construction to a multicellular one permitted animals to become larger. With multicellularity came a greater need for coordination; with the increase in size came a greater need for the conduction of information within the organism. To meet this need, certain cells of the multicellular organism specialized in enhancing both its irritability and the rapid conduction of changes in irritability through the animal. With further specialization, these cells became so organized that there grew up a division of labor to detect environmental change (both inside and outside the organism), to conduct information, to integrate information, and to initiate a response. These cells became the nervous system, the matrix of behavior. It follows that an organism's behavior is an expression principally of the capabilities of its nervous system.

The study of animal behavior is, therefore, an analysis of the potentialities of the nervous system. Note that we say "potentialities" rather than "physiology" of the nervous system, since we want to emphasize that the nervous system affects the whole animal or an organ system of the animal and controls the animal's changing relations with its environment. The nervous system does not operate in a vacuum. It is affected by the limitations and biases imprinted upon it during its long evolutionary history, by its particular stage of development in the growing individual, by the changes impressed upon it by its own repeated performance, and by the influence of internal and external environmental changes. Ultimately, its actions are translated into some effect outside itself.

The main function of the nervous system is to control the release of energy through the contraction of muscles and the secretions of glands; it also regulates such other forms of energy as light (the firefly) and electromotive force (the electric eel). Of these effects, muscular movement is surely the most widespread and important. Until complex muscular systems evolved, intricate behavior was impossible even though the nervous system may have possessed the potentiality for such behavior. The control of muscular energy involves more than mere efficiency of contractile mechanisms. The contractions of the various muscles must be synchronized so that their work is directed to serve the requirements of the animal. Otherwise there is a useless waste of energy. Muscular movements differ widely in complexity: in their frequency, in their sequential relationships, in their duration, in their intensities, in their over-all patterns of action, in their influence on other movements, in the circumstances that initiate them, and in their reactions to previous effects.

To understand behavior we must look first at certain aspects of the nervous system. We must examine its role in recording changes in the environment, in assessing this information, and in coordinating the various muscular activities that will best serve the economical operation of the animal. But our search for understanding will not end with the nervous system, because we shall discover that the nervous system, in activating the muscles, the glands, and other effectors, indirectly acts upon itself— for example, when part of the nervous system causes a muscle to contract, the action of the muscle stimulates other nerves which then may terminate the initial action. Our search, therefore, will extend to these other systems, the glands and muscles, for it is from the interplay of all these systems that behavior is made.

Irritability
and Conduction

CHAPTER ONE

From protoplasmic irritability to cognition is a development that has required upwards of a billion years. This development is inextricably bound to the evolution of the nervous system. In the beginning, of course, there was no nervous system. Isolated masses of living material probably showed general and uniform irritability. Whenever a stimulus caused a change at one point, this change undoubtedly stimulated adjacent areas so that a wave of excitation spread slowly in all directions, like the ripples from a stone dropped in a quiet pool.

Through the course of time, the property of irritability gradually tended to be localized, channeled, and refined so that the organism was no longer equally excitable throughout. The conduction of excitation was speeded and channeled into particular pathways. The advantages of this refinement are clear, since otherwise the organism would be a constantly reacting thing lacking versatility and finesse of discrimination. In the course of evolution, irritability has been channeled in two broad directions: In one, elaboration took place at a subcellular level within the confines of a single plasma membrane; in the other, elaboration occurred at a cellular level, and a multicellular structure developed.

ACELLULAR CONDUCTING SYSTEMS

In the protozoa of today, great differences in complexity exist, from the relatively undifferentiated protoplasmic mass of an ameba to the elaborate organelle system of the ciliates, e.g., *Paramecium*. The protoplasm in the ciliates consists of areas specialized for detecting changes in the environment, other areas designed for conducting excitation to various parts of the body, and still others for producing limited and local responses. These specialized areas include sensory bristles, photoreceptors, cilia for swimming, cirri (fused cilia) for crawling, food-catching devices, organelles for attachment, trichocysts (microscopic harpoon-like structures believed to assist in the holding of prey), contractile fibrils (*myonemes*) that may even be cross-striated, and fibrils whose function is presumed to be conduction. Figure 1-1 illustrates an experiment designed to show the function of these fibrils.

We do not fully understand the actions of these relatively elaborate systems, but irritability in them is essentially part of a single structure. The inherent intimacy of the structure sets limits on the complexity of the mechanism, on the scope of its performance, and, above all, on its potentiality.

Acellular systems are, however, obviously capable of serving the primary needs of the animal for food, protection, and reproduction. To fulfill these needs, the animal must be able to move and to detect environmental features. All these functions may be performed by relatively undifferentiated protoplasm, such as an ameba. The ameba's sensory world seems to be divided into food and nonfood. Virtually all stimuli that are not food elicit withdrawal reactions; food (and some chemicals) initiate

Fig. 1-1. When an incision is made in the ciliate Euplotes in such a way as to cut the fibrils (f.) running from the motorium (m.) (spot where activity originates) to the cirri (c.), coordination of locomotion is lost (A). Other incisions (B) do not interfere with locomotion. (Redrawn from Taylor, Univ. Calif. Pub. Zool., 19, 1920, 403–470.)

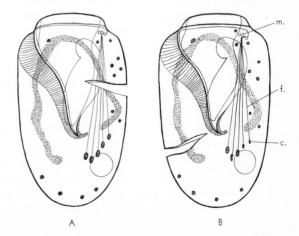

A   B

feeding responses. How the ameba captures food depends on what kind of food it is, how active the food is, and whether the ameba is sated or unfed. Amebae exhibit almost no other patterns of behavior. These appear to be the behavioral limitations of undifferentiated protoplasm.

With the development of organelles, somewhat more complicated reactions may take place. Cilia, flagella, contractile fibrils (myonemes), and specialized sensory areas permit a greater variety of behavior than do all-purpose pseudopodia. For example, directed orientation to light is possible in the green flagellate *Euglena* because it has a light-sensitive eyespot and an opaque spot called a stigma. We can show by passing a shadow over the eyespot that it is indeed sensitive to light. *Euglena* can perform directed (as opposed to random) movements because the eyespot is periodically shaded by the stigma as the transparent organism rotates in swimming, and thus the comparison of intensities (i.e., light and no light) necessary for orientation is possible. Protozoa generally cannot perform oriented movements. Stimuli elicit from protozoa movements whose direction bears no relation to the location of the stimulus. In most flagellates and ciliates, any stimulus that is not favorable causes the animal to back away, turn its body aside, and then to resume its forward movement. This avoiding reaction of *Paramecium* is stereotyped; it lacks individuality and originality.

Although protozoa show only a limited number of reactions, the acellular plan of construction does permit a wide latitude of performance. Consider, for example, the differences among species. Some ciliates swim in a monotonous random fashion; others show a complicated exploratory behavior. *Stichotricha,* for example, lives in a cell of a duckweed (*Lemna*) leaf where it divides to produce two individuals. One of these extends its front end through the aperture of the cell to feed, while the other, the swarmer, spends most of its early life wandering about inside the cell and eventually pushes its companion out of the way and emerges through the aperture. If it encounters an abundance of duckweed, it crawls over the leaves and pokes into or enters empty cells. If, on the other hand, little duckweed is immediately available, the swarmer makes long swimming excursions until it finds some.

Stalked protozoa such as *Stentor* and *Vorticella* exhibit even more complicated behavior. To a light touch that is continued for a time, the animal may first respond by contracting on its stalk, but it finally becomes indifferent to the stimulus. To repeated touches, it may show a series of reactions. It may first bend, then momentarily reverse its ciliary beat, then contract into its tube, then release its hold and swim away. The order of responses is not fixed, but each tends to remove the animal from the range of the stimulus; that is, all are adaptive. *Stentor* also tends to be selective in its feeding. But as it gets hungrier, it becomes less selective.

The actions of protozoa are characterized not only by responsiveness to external change but also by spontaneous change, that is, by constant unrest, such as the rhythmic action of cilia and the rhythmic contraction of such stalked forms as *Vorticella*. Since the organism is unresting, external stimuli do not operate against a constant background, but against a shifting one. This makes the condition of the animal itself significant in determining how it will react to a given stimulus. Since change leaves its mark, any reactions depend on past events. If *Paramecium,* for instance, has fed on carmine particles for a while, it may later reject them and continue doing so for two to three days. Animals that have been stimulated repeatedly may eventually become indifferent to the stimulus. Stalked protozoa, on the other hand, may give a variety of responses to a continuing stimulus. Here, then, is the first indication that behavior is capable of being modified.

Whether protozoa are capable of learning is still a debated question. It has been reported, for example, that ameba and *Paramecia* are capable of habituation to noxious sensory stimuli such as strong light or mechanical shock, for upon repeated stimulations their responses grow weaker and weaker until in some cases the animals become totally unresponsive. Two criticisms of this work have been offered, however. One is that none of these experiments has satisfactorily demonstrated that such diminished responses lasted long enough to be anything more than adaptations to sensory stimuli. The other is simply that the noxious stimulation may have temporarily injured the organisms, rendering them less capable of responding with each successive stimulation.

To get around these objections, attempts have been made to demonstrate some form of associative conditioning or learning. But each claim has again been met with cogent criticisms. One experiment will serve to illustrate the point. First a sterile platinum wire was lowered into the center of a dish of *Paramecia*. There was no special reaction to it. Next the wire was "baited" with bacteria, and the *Paramecia* responded by congregating around the wire, clinging to it and feeding. Then, after many such presentations of the "baited" wire, it was sterilized and dipped into the same spot, and the *Paramecia* again congregated around it and clung to it. This was claimed to be a well-controlled demonstration of the learning of a new response to the sterile wire. A simple control, however, demonstrated that the training was unnecessary. In this control experiment, bacteria were dropped into the dish and the *Paramecia* congregated and fed. Then the sterile platinum wire was lowered for the first time into the same spot as the bacteria had been, and the *Paramecia* clung to it. Careful investigation showed that the congregation around the spot the wire touched was due to the residue of bacteria bait. The increased clinging to the wire resulted from the increased acidity the bacteria contributed to the medium, since further controls showed that clinging in *Paramecia* was a function of acidity.

MULTICELLULAR CONDUCTING SYSTEMS

The multicellular animal is essentially an interrupted system, since the cells of which it is constructed are more or less self-contained units. It is a brick building as opposed to one of poured concrete. Irritability in a multicellular organism thus resides in many discrete units, each capable of different levels of sensitivity and different rates of change. Each may be responsive to different kinds of change in its environment, may require different periods for recovery, and may deliver different kinds of energy by way of response. These units retain a certain independence of action, but they also affect one another to varying degrees.

Multicellular construction makes possible an almost infinite number of combinations of units with a high level of sensitivity. A state of excitation set up at any one point in a sensitive unit can spread rapidly to all parts of it. When one unit comes into sufficiently close contact with another, the excitation is transmitted across the union. This system of many specialized parts, therefore, can attain a complexity and fluidity that is denied the unitary acellular system. We may now begin to call this arrangement of cells that is specialized for irritability and conduction, the nervous system. Its structural development throughout the animal kingdom has involved the differentiation, shuffling, ordering, and combining of cells.

THE NEURON

The unit of the nervous system is the *neuron* (the nerve cell body plus all its protoplasmic outgrowths). The average neuron is slightly less than 1/10 mm in diameter, just beyond the visual range. Although neurons come in all shapes and sizes, they consist typically of three major parts: dendrites, which normally receive excitation and conduct it to the cell body; the cell body, which contains the nucleus; and the axon (nerve fiber), which normally transmits excitation away from the cell body (Fig. 1-2). The neuron is an extraordinarily sensitive cell, and excitation at one point spreads rapidly to all parts even though the axon may extend a distance of many feet, as, for example, a sensory cell that reaches from the toe to the brain.

THE NERVE IMPULSE

That excitation is actually conducted along an axon is amply demonstrated if we pinch (or otherwise stimulate) a fiber whose far end is attached to a muscle. The muscle contracts. Experiments have shown that the passage of such a nerve impulse is accompanied by an electrical change (the action potential) that is a few hundredths or thousandths of a volt in magnitude and a few thousandths of a second in duration. The impulse may travel as fast as 200 miles per hour (in the thickest nerves

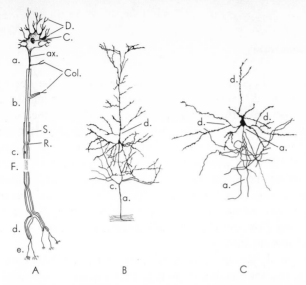

Fig. 1-2. (A) Diagram of a motor neuron, showing the cell body, C., dendrites, D.; axon, ax.; collaterals, Col.; Schwann's sheath, S.; node of Ranvier, R.; area of naked axon, a.; area of axon invested only with myelin, b.; area of axon invested with Schwann's sheath and myelin, c.; broken lines indicating the great extent of the axon, F.; area in which the axon is covered only with Schwann's sheath and its nuclei, d.; area of the naked axon ending in an arborization, e. (B) A pyramidal neuron from the cerebral cortex of a rabbit: axon, a.; collateral branches, c.; dendrite, d. (C) Type II neuron from the cerebral cortex of a cat: axon, a.; dendrites, d. (Redrawn from Maximow and Bloom, A Textbook of Histology. Philadelphia: Saunders, 1941, 169–172.)

of man). The nerve impulse is *not* an electric current passing down the nerve, rather it is a complex cycle of electrochemical changes in nerve structure; we shall describe these briefly below. Neurons are highly specialized for conducting impulses. All nerves are similar in this respect.

Since the nerve impulse is the language of behavior, we should know something of its basic properties. These can be studied by placing electrodes on nerves and observing the changes that occur when the nerves are stimulated. If we place one electrode on the outside of an unstimulated neuron, insert a second inside, and connect the two to an instrument that will record electrical current, we will see that the outside of the neuron is electrically positive with respect to the inside. The neuron is thus said to be polarized. When it is stimulated (pinched, shocked electrically, covered with chemicals, subjected to drastic temperature changes, etc.), it responds because it is constructed of protoplasm, one of whose basic properties is irritability (responding to change). The response consists of a change in the permeability of the surface membrane, which permits ions to flow into the axon from the surrounding fluid (Fig. 1-3).

As a result of this flow, the electrical difference between the inside and outside of the neuron changes. The nerve is then depolarized. If the area or degree of depolarization is small, the nerve uses its energy of metabolism to restore the membrane to its former polarized state, and no nerve impulse is generated. If, on the other hand, the degree of depolarization is great, the nerve cannot restore itself immediately; consequently, electric current flows from the intact areas on either side of the depolarized spot. This flow causes these areas to become depolarized in turn. In other words, the nerve is now stimulating itself. The process continues so that the state of depolarization moves away from the original site in both directions along the nerve. This combination of membrane changes, chemical changes, and electrical changes *all together constitute the nerve impulse.* The nerve impulse is usually described, however, in terms of the traveling electrical change (called the *action potential*), since it is the easiest change to measure.

The action potential has an all-or-none character. In other words, if it occurs at all, it has the maximum voltage that the axon can produce. Furthermore, it travels along the nerve without any loss of amplitude because it is constantly generated at each point by the neuron. Since the neuron generates the action potential, its characteristics are determined by the nerve and not by the stimulus that began the whole series of events. The situation is roughly analogous to the firing of a gun. The stimulus (the finger on the trigger) produces a pressure (the local excitatory state) that causes the firing pin to release the energy stored in the gun powder and start the bullet on its way. Whether the pressure on the trigger (the stimulus) is fast or slow, produced by a finger or a hammer does not affect the flight of the bullet.

A nerve is not equally excitable at all times. After an impulse is generated, the nerve is less sensitive and must recover before another impulse

Fig. 1-3. The relation between the local electrical response (dashed line) caused by a stimulus and the action potential generated from it, as seen on the screen of a cathode ray oscilloscope attached to two electrodes recording electrical events in a single nerve fiber. The action potential is diphasic because it is being recorded by two electrodes. The local electrical response and the action potential were produced in succession and then superimposed to show their relationship. (Redrawn from Hodgkin, J. Physiol., **90**, 1937, 183–232.)

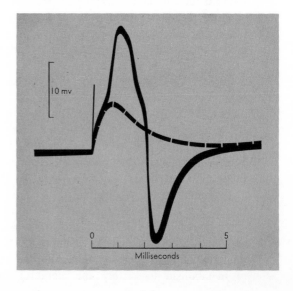

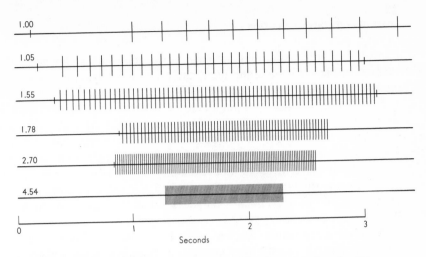

Fig. 1-4. The repetitive responses of a single motor fiber from a crab under constant stimulation. The frequency of response increases with the strength of stimulus proportional to the numbers. Note that the amplitude of the action potential does not change. (Redrawn from Hodgkin, J. Physiol., **107**, 1948, 165–181.)

can be generated. Thus, nerve impulses occur as pulses or volleys, even though the stimulus initiating them may be continuous (Fig. 1-4).

SYNAPSES

We have already pointed out that nerve cells are distinct entities. The places where they come together, where the ends of the axon of one cell come into close contact with the cell body and dendrites of other cells, are called *synapses*. Synapses may be very complex structures. The terminations of many axons may impinge upon a cell (Fig. 1-5), or a pro-

Fig. 1-5. Synapses. (A) A motor nerve cell showing many presynaptic fibers (p.f.) ending on the same cell. (Redrawn from Lorente de No, J. Neurophysiol., **1**, 1938, 194.) (B) Three neurons from a stellate ganglion showing the network of presynaptic fibers associated with them. Redrawn from de Castro, Cytology and Cellular Pathology of the Nervous System. **New York: Hoeber, 1932.)**

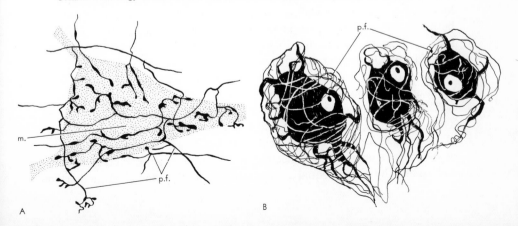

A   B

fusely branching axon may impinge upon many cells. Because of the many possible kinds of connections, the presence of synapses in a nervous system introduces great complexities into the pathways over which impulses may travel, just as a multitude of switches in a railroad yard permits more complicated movement of trains than do straight tracks alone. Even greater complexity can occur in the nervous system than in a freight yard, however, because the synapses are not simple switches that all work in the same fashion. For example, transmission across synapses occurs in one direction only; different synapses delay transmission differently; and synapses eventually fatigue so that they may fail to transmit for a time.

An even more subtle characteristic of synapses, *summation,* adds still greater complexity to the nervous system. Summation takes place as follows. Excitation crossing the synaptic gap may be insufficient to initiate an impulse in the postsynaptic cell. Repeated excitation of the same strength, however, may succeed; that is, the successive excitations add (temporal summation). Also, excitation from one presynaptic fiber may fail to excite the postsynaptic fiber, whereas simultaneous excitations from many may succeed; they add in space (spatial summation).

The over-all effect of summation is called *facilitation;* that is, excitation too weak in itself to cause an effect may facilitate other excitation that also could accomplish nothing by itself. A reverse situation occurs at some synapses where excitation in one fiber blocks synaptic transmission to another (*inhibition*). Inhibition is just as important in nervous coordination as excitation is. In short, as we shall see later, it is the aforementioned functional characteristics and spatial interrelations of synapses that make integrated action by the nervous system possible.

RECEPTORS

Although some neurons are spontaneously active, discharging without apparent stimulation, most impulses in a neuron arise as a result of stimulation by another neuron or by some change in the environment. The cells that respond to changes in the environment are called *receptors.* Receptors may be free nerve endings of the sort that register pain or they may be nerve cells or fibers associated with very complex accessory structures, such as those that go to make up the eye or the ear. By virtue of its specialized structure, a sense organ is usually sensitive to only one kind of stimulus; the eye *normally* responds to light but will also respond to electrical and mechanical stimulation.

The stimulus, the change in the environment, is some form of energy. Thus, light is detected by means of a pigment that absorbs the energy of photons of certain energy; heat is detected by absorption of photons of a different energy level; electricity, by the energy of electrons; tastes and smells, by the potential energy existing in the mutual attraction and repulsion of the particles making up atoms; sound, by the energy of moving particles of molecular size. The energy in each case causes a local excitatory state in the receptor. This local excitatory state generates an action potential that travels along the connecting nerve. Although the receptor may be specific, the message it sends along the nerve is not. All messages in all nerves are alike in that they are nerve impulses. The stimulus, regardless of its nature, sends only a message that that particular organ was stimulated. If the stimulus was intense, the impulses are close together; if weak, the impulses are less frequent (Fig. 1-4). The intensity of stimulation, in short, is signaled by the frequency of impulses (each of which fires in an all-or-none fashion) in a fiber and, since different fibers have different sensitivities, by the number of fibers responding. Under continuous stimulation, the sensitivity of a fiber decreases so that the frequency of firing gradually diminishes. This decrease in frequency under constant stimulation is called *adaptation*. The quality of sensation (light, smell, touch) depends on the nature of the connections the sensory nerve make within the nervous system. The relations among stimulus, neuronal events, and sensation are illustrated in Fig. 1-6.

Most animals have mechanoreceptors (responding to mechanical deformation) that are sensitive to stretch, compression, and torque; chemoreceptors sensitive to tastes and odors; humidity receptors sensitive to water vapor; and photoreceptors sensitive to various wavelengths of light. A steady flow of information from mechanoreceptors is necessary for an animal to maintain normal posture; to walk, swim, or fly; to feed; and to

Fig. 1-6. Diagram showing the relations among the stimulus, the local excitatory state, the action potential, and sensation. (Redrawn from Adrian, The Basis of Sensation. **London: Christophers, 1949.)**

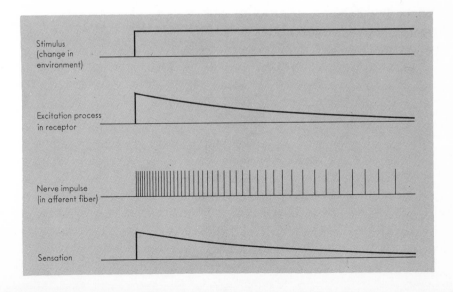

manipulate its environment (e.g., dig burrows, build nests). Mechano-receptors are also important in supplying information for the proper working of many internal organs. Hearing, a form of mechanoreception, is important in many animals for courtship, advertising their territory, warning, and orientation by echolocation (as in bats and porpoises). Detection of tastes and odors is important in all feeding activities, many sexual and reproductive activities, social activities, and such forms of orientation as involve trail following.

Clearly, the nervous system does not sit idly by in a state of passive rest. Because of the spontaneous activity of many neurons, it is in a state of continous background activity. Messages coming in from the sense organs in contact with the external and internal environment may be thought of as constantly modulating this background activity. It is the interaction of background activity and messages from sense organs that produces behavior.

Simple
Nervous Systems

CHAPTER TWO

Almost from the beginning, two major trends have been evident in the evolving nervous system: one toward a division of labor, in which different neurons or their parts become specialized for different jobs, the other toward segregation, in which like units become grouped together. The over-all effect of this grouping has been a tendency toward centralization.

NET AND RADIAL NERVOUS SYSTEMS

The nervous system made its first appearance in the hydras, jellyfish, sea anemones, and corals (Coelenterata). Even that early in its history it had evolved from a condition of uniformity and complete diffusion to one in which there was a considerable division of labor and almost the maximum degree of centralization permitted by a radial plan of body construction.

The nervous system is seen in its simplest form in *Hydra,* where it consists of three functional divisions: cells (receptors) that sense changes in the environment, cells that conduct excitation to various parts of the body, and cells (effectors) that respond to these changes by movement. Not all the surface of *Hydra* is equally sensitive to changes in the environment. Certain epithelial cells (receptors) (Fig. 2-1) that occur singly or in patches on the external surface and on the internal surface that is in contact with food are especially sensitive to mechanical and chemical changes. Other sense cells (epitheliomuscular cells) (Fig. 2-2) have flattened bases equipped with contractile fibers. Whereas the simple sense cells transmit excitation through their basal fibers to other cells, the epitheliomuscular cells transform the energy of the stimulus into work; that is, their bases contract. They are thus said to be independent effectors. *Hydra,* and other coelenterates as well, possess, in addition, nonnervous, independent effectors that are of great importance in behavior. These cells (nematocysts) consist of small harpoon-like structures that are capable of being discharged when properly stimulated.

The simple sense cells transmit their excitation either to the second element of the nervous system, the conducting elements, or directly to the muscles. Aside from independent effectors, a direct connection between sense cells and muscle is the simplest possible association between sensing element and working unit. It allows very little flexibility of action. On the other hand, when the sense cell ties into the conducting system, far more varied behavior is possible because of the increased number and complexity of connections with effectors.

Considerable mystery still surrounds the conducting system in *Hydra*. Although the electronmicroscope shows no neurons, silver and methylene blue stains reveal neuron-like cells. They are unipolar, bipolar,

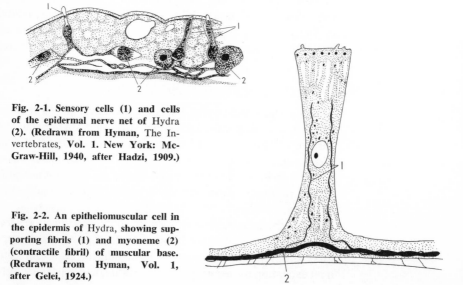

Fig. 2-1. Sensory cells (1) and cells of the epidermal nerve net of Hydra (2). (Redrawn from Hyman, The Invertebrates, Vol. 1. New York: McGraw-Hill, 1940, after Hadzi, 1909.)

Fig. 2-2. An epitheliomuscular cell in the epidermis of Hydra, showing supporting fibrils (1) and myoneme (2) (contractile fibril) of muscular base. (Redrawn from Hyman, Vol. 1, after Gelei, 1924.)

and multipolar. They conduct slow (20–50 msec.) action potentials. In some coelenterates the net is believed to be continuous and unbroken (syncytium), but in *Hydra* it is believed that the cells never lose their identity even though they come extraordinarily close together. This arrangement appears to be a synaptic system, yet it does not exhibit all the characteristics of one. For instance, it does not possess one-way transmission nor does it transmit without loss in strength. One portion of the network lies close to the external surface of the animal (as does the conducting system of protozoa); the other portion lines the gastric cavity. All parts of the animal are in slow communication with one another through the maze-like web. Since cell bodies and processes are about equally distributed through the organism, one part of the system is essentially like another. But it was probably a system like this, which in *Hydra* forms an indiscriminate communications network, that gave rise to the central nervous system of higher animals.

The third important element in the behavior of *Hydra* is the muscular system, which is composed of the dual-function epitheliomuscular cells already mentioned and single-celled contractile units that are greatly extended and branched and so form thin muscular sheets. These cells, like all muscle cells, are contractile units with a high level of irritability. For work to be done, the irritability must be altered in some way to set off the contractile mechanism. The function of the nervous system is to affect the irritability.

Sea anemones look like larger and more complicated *Hydra,* and are essentially that from a nervous and muscular point of view. Structurally, their nervous system is not appreciably more complex. It is, however, more synaptic in nature, that is, the neurons are not only more clearly separated but are functionally more discrete. They also consist primarily of bipolar cells whose axons tend to run in parallel courses instead of in all directions as in *Hydra*. The greatest advance, however, lies in the effector system. Instead of being isolated fibers, the muscles are organized into circular and longitudinal muscle cylinders. The arrangement of muscles and mesenteries (supporting tissues) is such that these animals tend to be bilaterally rather than radially symmetrical.

CENTRALIZATION IN JELLYFISH

In animals that are radially symmetrical, any development of the nervous system toward centralization clearly will be molded by the basic symmetry of the body and, as a moment's thought will reveal, will also be constrained by that symmetry. The maximum degree of centralization that can be achieved is seen in the hydroid medusae (jellyfish) and in starfishes and their relatives.

The nerve network in the jellyfish is channeled into two nerve rings in the bell, or umbrella, an arrangement made possible when some processes of the neurons became longer than others and were grouped into parallel

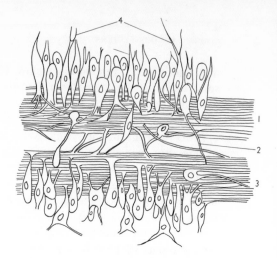

Fig. 2-3. Fine structure of the nerve ring of the jellyfish Goni-onemus: (1) upper nerve, (2) fibers crossing to lower nerve (3), (4) connecting fibrils to subumbrella net. (Redrawn from Hyman, Vol. 1, after Phyde, 1902.)

bundles (Fig. 2-3). Such an arrangement permits speedy directional conduction rather than slow diffusion. The large upper ring receives fibers from the sense organs in the margin of the bell and also supplies the musculature that activates the bell. The two rings are connected by a network of neurons (plexus).

The first true sense organs in the invertebrates are found in the jellyfish. One kind (ocelli) respond to light; another kind (statocysts) to changes in position. The ocelli (Fig. 2-4) are patches of pigment cells that may be cup-shaped and equipped with a lens-like body and are interspersed with nerve cells. The statocysts (Fig. 2-5) are groups of sensory cells associated with a round concretion of organic material and calcium carbonate.

TYPES OF BEHAVIOR

Fig. 2-4. The complex ocellus of a jellyfish: (1) exumbrella epidermis, (2) subumbrella epidermis, (3) sensory epithelium, (4) pigment cup of ocellus, (5) statocyst, (6) velum. (Redrawn from Hyman, Vol. 1, after Linko, 1900.)

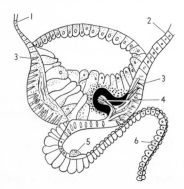

The structures described in the previous paragraphs are the sensing and responding systems with which the coelenterates have to work in coping with their environment. Most of their behavior is concerned with feeding, locomotion, and protection from noxious stimuli. The behavior varies in complexity from rather simple patterns in the small stalked species like *Hydra* through more complicated movements in the stalked sea anemones, culminating in the complex behavior of such free-swimming medusae as *Gonionemus*. In general, all responses are slow and stereotyped, and isolated fragments of the animal respond as well as the animal as a whole.

In the presence of adverse stimuli, the general behavior pattern is one of slow contraction of all or part of the body, depending on the point of contact of the stimulus and its intensity. The mechanism has been carefully studied in the case of protective closure of the oral disc of the sea anemone (*Calliactis parasitica*). Closure is obviously a response that protects the delicate disc and tentacles from injury. The sensitivity of the sphincter muscles is low and adaptation is rapid. Messages are transmitted fairly rapidly from the site of stimulation through the nerve net. The speed is possible because the organism has a through-conducting system—that is, certain neural pathways that conduct in an all-or-none manner without hindrance. Somewhere in the system facilitation occurs—that is, one nerve impulse does not normally cause the muscles to contract; bursts of impulses are required. The low sensitivity, rapid adaptation, and facilitation are all characteristics that insure response only when absolutely required.

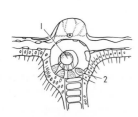

Fig. 2-5. Closed type of statocyst that is found in the jellyfish Obelia: (1) statolith, (2) sensory cells. (Redrawn from Hyman, Vol. 1, after the Hertwigs, 1878.)

Feeding behavior may be even more complicated than the mechanism just described. In *Hydra* it involves these steps: The tentacles grasp solid objects, the nematocysts discharge, the objects are conveyed to the mouth, the mouth opens to receive the food, the tentacles relax after the food has reached the mouth, the rim of the mouth glides over the food to encompass it, after which the mouth closes, the distal part of the column undergoes circular contraction forcing the food into the middle region, the food is retained from one-half to several hours, and eventually indigestible material is rejected. The fine coordination and the anticipatory opening of the mouth seem to be impossible feats for a simple net nervous system. We still do not understand the mechanism of feeding, although careful studies of nematocysts have shed some light on the problem. There are four types of nematocysts in *Hydra,* each with a different function. In two types the threshold is lowered (sensitivity increased) by chemicals diffusing from the food so that prey bumping into the tentacles elicits an immediate response. One of these two types of nematocyst entangles prey and holds it; the second, discharging later, penetrates and kills the prey. In the third type chemicals from food raise the threshold to touch so that firing does not occur in the presence of food. These nematocysts are employed in locomotion. Accordingly, food inhibits locomotion. A fourth kind of nematocyst has its threshold to touch lowered by diffusible substances from noxious animals and thus is employed in defense.

It was formerly believed that *Hydra* was restricted to living prey from Nemathelminthes or higher phyla and that the feeding reaction depended exclusively on stimulation by glutathione released from wounded prey. These conclusions have not been substantiated. *Hydra* feeds on many things, including filter paper soaked in beef broth, protozoa, algae, and mud.*

In *Metridium,* feeding behavior is more than just a simple succession of responses to stimuli. As in *Hydra,* it consists of a preparatory behavior, a discharge of nematocysts, and movements conveying food to the mouth. The presence of food juices in the vicinity often induces a characteristic preparatory movement arising from the alternate contractions of the longitudinal and circular muscles. The disc expands, the stalk elongates, and the animal may make swaying movements. All these movements increase the animal's chances of coming into contact with food. Each element of the pattern involves the coordinated activity of several muscle systems, which have long latency and smooth contraction. Elongation involves the reciprocal inhibition and successive activation of two antagonistic muscle systems, the circular muscles and the longitudinal muscles. The final act involves the reflex movements that carry food to the mouth.

The preparatory feeding movements of *Metridium* are not a unique pattern brought about by stimulation; they are a modification of movements that are going on in the animal all the time, even in the absence of stimulation. Sea anemones in a constant environment show rhythmic spontaneous activity, which is, however, so slow that it can be observed only by the use of time-lapse photography. This activity is produced by the alternate contraction of the longitudinal and circular muscles, the same ones employed in the preparatory movements. In *Hydra,* spontaneous movements are few, but contractions and expansions do occur at intervals without apparent cause, and the tentacles may move about.

Spontaneous activity is the basis of the swimming movements in such jellyfish as *Gonionemus,* where by vigorous contraction of the ventral surface of the animal, water is forced rhythmically out of the bell. Experiments have shown that the origin of activity is the nerve ring, for when the ring is cut, the coordination of the movements of the bell is destroyed, although small pieces of the ring and attached bell continue to contract rhythmically after separation from the animal. Ingenious cutting experiments with jellyfish and with sea anemones demonstrate strikingly that, in the latter, normal contraction of the animal is not hindered. These results indicate that the nerve net of anemones conducts in a diffuse manner in many directions, whereas in the jellyfish the origin of the wave of excitation is in the marginal bodies, those cell concentrations consisting of a statocyst and grouped neurons. If all marginal bodies but one are removed, a cut can be made in such a way that the wave of excitation will be tapped. Such a wave courses around the bell in a circular path for as long as eleven days, during

* For a complete discussion see *Biol. Bull.* 122: 343, 1962.

which it travels over 450 miles. Such experiments show not only that conduction is channeled but also that at this evolutionary stage, the nervous system has groups of neurons that have endogenous rhythmic activity and act as pacemakers.

The spontaneous movements exhibited by coelenterates are by no means constant. They vary with the condition of the animal. *Hydra,* for example, when deprived of food for some time extends its stalk, increases the movements of its tentacles, and eventually moves from its place of attachment. It moves by any one of three methods: by basal gliding (a mechanism not clearly understood), by pulling itself along by the tentacles, or by looping and somersaulting. *Gonionemus,* when deprived of food, "fishes," by swimming to the surface of the water, turning upside down, and then floating slowly downward with the tentacles widely extended. It may do this for hours.

The behavior of these animals is clearly being modified by internal conditions. When coelenterates are food-sated, the nematocysts will no longer discharge. When animals have been stimulated repeatedly in such a way as to cause contraction, they eventually cease to contract. In these and other instances, the results can be satisfactorily explained by sensory adaptation. There is no unequivocal evidence of learning of a higher order, however.

Here, then, are behavior patterns that are simple, stereotyped, slow, and sometimes representative of modifications of an endogenous activity of the simple nervous system. Complexity of behavior is clearly related to the development of the musculature, the degree to which the nervous system departs from a simple nerve net, and the degree of specialization of sense organs and independent effectors. Where the net is undifferentiated and the muscles isolated, there are few reflexes, and a part of the animal is nearly as efficient as the whole. Where the muscular system has become complicated and the nervous system concentrated into through-conduction pathways, as in the swimming medusae, the action of the individual parts has become coordinated. The coordination stems primarily from the topographical arrangement of nerves. In the coelenterates also we see for the first time an example of the degree of nonnervous coordination (the nematocysts) that can be achieved by differential response to chemicals.

Complex Radial Nervous Systems

Coelenterates did not exhaust the potentialities of a radial nervous system, even when they abandoned sessile life for freedom of motion. The ultimate in radial nervous systems was achieved by the echinoderms (sea cucumbers, sea urchins, and starfish). Neither tentacular nor umbrellar movement had given the nervous system much latitude for change. With the development of tube feet in sea urchins and starfish and with the added freedom of movement permitted by arms in the starfish (especially the brittle stars) coincident with a more diversified nervous system, behavior achieved considerable versatility. One of the great advances of the nervous system was the increase and ordering of the neurons between the sense organs and effectors. As the nerve net began to condense into nerve tracts and to move away from its location near the surface of the animal, the distances between receptors and effectors became greater. Direct synapses between receptors and effectors disappeared as additional neurons came into being to make connections. These intermediate neurons, the internuncials or associational neurons, made possible a variety of connections between sensory (afferent) neurons and motor (efferent) and thus, by providing more synapses and alternate pathways, enhanced enormously the capabilities of the nervous system.

THE SEA CUCUMBER NERVOUS SYSTEM

Various steps in the evolution of these developments are preserved in the echinoderms. Sea cucumbers have not advanced far. They have a nerve ring surrounding the buccal (mouth) cavity, nerves to the tentacles (when tentacles are present), five radial nerves supplying muscle fibers of the body wall, and a general body plexus. This system is consonant with the uninspired behavior exhibited by these sluggish animals, whose repertory consists essentially of moving the tentacles for food, righting themselves when upset, and burrowing in the ocean bottom.

THE STARFISH NERVOUS SYSTEM

The basic plan of the nervous system in starfish is similar to that of sea cucumbers, consisting of a circumoral ring, a radial nerve to each of the five arms, and a dermal plexus. In detailed anatomy, however, it is wondrously complex, being differentiated not only into sense cells and motor neurons, but also into associational neurons, nerve tracts, and reflex arcs of various degrees of intricacy. Many of the activities of starfish can be understood in terms of these units. The relationship among them illustrates how strikingly behavior is a function of the nervous system.

The outer surface of a starfish is equipped with spines and pincer-like structures (pedicellariae) which can hold and paralyze small animals that come into contact with them. The outer ectoderm consists of epithelial cells, mucus glands, and about 4000 sensory cells per square millimeter of surface. Lying beneath these cells is a nerve plexus, the outer layer of which consists of randomly arranged fibers in synaptic connection with the sensory epithelium. Still deeper, the plexus is organized into linear tracts. All of this structure lies outside the thick, fibrous stroma that constitutes the main bulk of the body wall. Where thin spots exist in the body wall between the ossicles, synaptic connection may occur with the motor part of the system that lies inside the stroma. The inner surface of the stroma—that is, the part facing the body cavity—is lined with epithelium where the muscles and motor fibers are located. Thus, the sensory system and associational pathways of the epidermis lie outside the stroma and the motor tracts lie inside.

The calcified plates of the arm are so situated that the arm, its associated nerve arcs and motor centers, and the tube feet are segmentally arranged (Fig. 3-1). Axons of the motor neurons in the radial nerve cord encircle the tube feet. They join a lateral motor center, the axons of which extend in three tracts to various parts of the arm. Here they make a number of synaptic connections that eventually reach the muscles.

ECHINODERM BEHAVIOR

The contributing roles of these differently organized parts of the nervous system are well illustrated by the different response patterns that are elicited when one spot on the dorsal surface of one of the arms is lightly pressed. First, the spines bend toward the spot, and the pedicellariae open and close their pincers. This response is extremely localized. It is certainly mediated through the dorsal plexus. In its action, it resembles the nerve net of coelenterates. The foot immediately below the spot that was stimulated is then activated. This response is regulated via the segmental arcs in which transmission is through-conducting and polarized (i.e., in one direction only). Next, adjacent feet respond as a result of extrasegmental transmission via the radial cord. Finally, excitation involves the radial cords and nerve ring, and coordinated movement follows. Thus we see two aspects of nervous control: one, peripheral and reflex; the other, central and generalized.

Much of the behavior of starfish is based on activities of the tube feet. In addition to being protracted and retracted, the tube feet make postural movements associated with stepping. Protraction and retraction are unoriented, wholly reflex responses. When a region near a foot is stimulated, the foot retracts; when a wave washes over the animal, all feet retract, not as a result of coordination, but as independent members all reacting to a common stimulus. Protraction and retraction are antagonistic movements that reflect reciprocal states of excitation and inhibition in the motor neurons of the foot. The neurons mediating postural movements, however, reflect changing states of central excitation.

Fig. 3-1. Diagrammatic representation of the nervous system of the starfish. Excitation from plexus is transmitted via the nerve cord to motor neurons (mot.p.) thence to neurons (mot.l.) thence via three main tracts (a, b, c); str, stroma; oss, ossicle; pl, plexus. (Redrawn from Smith, "Physiological Mechanisms in Animal Behaviour," Symposia, Soc. Exp. Biol., **IV**. New York: Academic Press, 1950.)

Obviously, if there were not some coordination of stepping activity, the starfish would never progress. The coordination of feet within a given arm is effected by a control center at the base of the arm. An arm whose feet are stepping in a distal direction is dominant and imposes its direction on the others. Excitation to all feet of the animal is thus through-conducted from the dominant center via circumoral and radial nerve tracts. In some species, there is a tendency for arm number

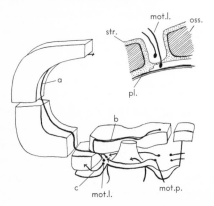

2 to lead most frequently. In all probability, some intrinsic feature of nervous organization, even possibly some retention of traces of bilaterality from larval days, is the basis of this behavior.

Generally, there are autonomous transfers of dominance from one foot to another. This suggests that there are periodic rises and falls of activity in the different centers. It is even possible that this might explain why starfish, given the problem of removing a rubber tube placed on one arm, may "solve" the problem in a variety of ways. These various levels of nervous activity and the waning and waxing of excitation may also explain how a starfish can right itself in a number of ways rather than by a single stereotyped method. It can, for example, right itself by somersaulting, folding over, or assuming a tulip form which causes it to flop over in an upright position.

In addition to righting themselves, echinoderms perform a number of other behavior patterns. Many starfish and sea urchins, for instance, exhibit a genuine brooding of eggs. In some cases the mother arches the disc so that it becomes concave on the oral side. The arms are pointed ventrally so that their bases form, with the concavity of the disk, a space in which eggs develop to the stage of tiny stars. Some sea urchins carry the young on the body. Many species characteristically burrow. Some bore into solid rock when they are small, enlarge the bottom of the hole as they grow, and live there permanently, being unable to get back out through the small hole made in their youth.

In relation to feeding, a variety of behavior patterns have been observed; the most common is that of the starfish that opens bivalve shellfish and digests the contents by everting its stomach. Some species of echinoderms are able to detect food from a distance. For example, one species of sea urchin, which lives in the sand in a burrow whose walls are plastered with mucus, keeps a pair of extensile appendages thrust through the surface hole and with widely opened terminal processes explores the sand surface, picking up food particles by way of adhesive secretion. The appendages then retract and deliver the food particles to the region of the mouth.

Some echinoderms also show defense reactions. Thus, sea urchins have a shadow reflex whereby spines are erected toward the source of danger. If the stimulus continues, the animal changes its behavior and retreats. The shadow reflex may be given by an isolated piece of shell. It is mediated by radial nerves, the nerve ring not being necessary.

Temporary modifications in behavior have been demonstrated in a number of different situations, but it has never been possible to rule out sensory adaptation, injury, or direct physical change as explanations of these modifications. For example, in one experiment with starfish, the animals were prevented from using their dominant rays in turning over by restraining them with a glass rod. The starfish used other rays to turn, and after 18 days of such treatment, 10 times a day, the nondominant rays were used in turning over, even though the glass rod was not applied. It was subsequently shown, however, that this same result could be obtained without the training procedure by simply irritating the dominant rays with mild acid or by rubbing them with the glass rod. After one or two such treatments, turning over was accomplished with the nondominant rays. Whether a starfish can learn to use any particular arm in righting itself or can profit by experience in escaping, for instance, from pegs inserted in angles between the arms is questionable.

SUMMARY

In our perusal of the animal kingdom thus far, we have observed a tendency toward the formation of specialized cells for selective response to environmental changes (receptors), the elaborations of these into groups associated with other tissues (sense organs), the development of specialized response systems (muscle cells and organized muscle sheets), and the channeling of conduction of excitation (nerve nets and nerve tracts). Specialization of function has gone hand in hand with a trend toward spatial separation. Sensory systems obviously tend to remain near the surface of the animal; response systems lie at deeper levels; consequently, the sensory and motor portions of the nervous system localize.

Conducting elements, which began as nerve networks lying close to the surface, in evolving sink into the animal and become the connecting link between receptors and effectors. Thus far in the evolutionary scale, the connections have been rather simple and direct. The number of neurons intervening between receptor and effector, however, seems to be increasing. These interneurons (internuncials) are, on the whole, not localized but are scattered in, and make up, the fiber tracts. The fiber tracts, which represent a condensation of the nerve network, are still made up of a mixture of fibers and their cell bodies.

These evolutionary developments have permitted animals to make more refined assessments of environmental changes, more diversified movements, more rapid, directed, and coordinated response. Despite these advances, however, the coelenterates and echinoderms remain animals with limited responses, a low level of coordination, and an absence of central control. Centralization of the nascent nervous system is severely restricted by the radially symmetrical body plan. In fact, no marked advances in nervous-system construction occurred until bilaterally symmetrical animals appeared on the scene.

Bilateral
Nervous Systems

With the assumption of a bilateral body plan, most animals acquired a longitudinal axis and a definite front and back. In this setting, the nervous system began a vital course of development whose end is not in sight and whose behavioral potentialities seem limitless. Evolutionary trends that were observed in radially symmetrical animals—namely, a functional division of the nervous system, condensation of the nerve net into more direct conductive pathways, and the interpolation of internuncials between sensory and motor systems as these moved farther apart—were perfected in bilaterally symmetrical animals. The refinement of sense organs, culminating in the exquisitely attuned olfactory receptors of insects, the vertebrate-like eye of the octopus, and the beautifully efficient compound eye of the dragonfly, continues in various branches of the animal kingdom. The problem of connecting nerves with muscles (neuromuscular mechanism) had been solved in a most efficient manner very early in evolution; hence, no further major changes took place. The effector system itself, the muscles, became more and more complex as animals developed articulated skeletons (external in the

27

invertebrates, internal in vertebrates) that permitted a versatility of movement heretofore unseen.

The truly great advance that bilaterality permitted was centralization of control. In simple animals, individual parts are rugged individualists; in complex animals, the parts have their actions subordinated to the activity of the whole. In the early stages of the evolutionary development of the nervous system, condensation of neural elements into centers occurred simultaneously in various parts of the body, but eventually the anterior end of the animal assumed more and more control as other centers became subordinated to it or lost. Although the net plan of innervation lost ground to a more centralized system, it was never completely abandoned. It is retained in some form for special purposes in almost all animals. Although it is essential for normal locomotion in echinoderms and lower chordates (e.g., balanoglossids), it is less important in annelids and molluscs. In the earthworm, it is probably a sensory relay system. In the mammalian intestine, a net is primarily responsible for coordination of peristaltic movement. Throughout the animal kingdom, then, where sluggish movements are called for, a diffuse, slowly conducting net is efficient.

Many of the stages of the evolutionary development of a bilateral nervous system are preserved in the existing animal forms, ranging from flatworms to arthropods. The beginnings of the system are to be found in the simplest flatworms (Acoela) and primitive molluscs (Chitons), where it is still a network located near the surface of the body. In some species, though, there is a faint suggestion of an anterior concentration of nervous tissue and a tendency toward developing the longitudinal strands of the net more strongly than strands running in other directions (Fig. 4-1A and B). The cells making up the strands have repressed the more or less equal develop-

Fig. 4-1. (A) Part of the submuscular plexus of a flatworm (Acoela) showing the statocyst (1) and the brain (2). (Redrawn from Hyman, Vol. 2.) (B) The nervous system of Chiton: buc. c., buccal commissure and ganglia; ce.c., cerebral commissure; p.v.c., palliovisceral commissure; ped.n., pedal ganglion and nerve; sb.rad.c., subradula commissure. (Redrawn from Borradaile and Potts, Invertebrata. New York: Macmillan, 1935.)

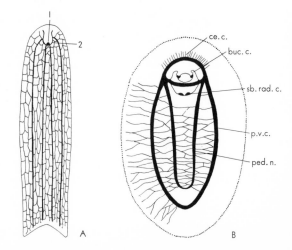

ment of all their extensions and have greatly elongated one process (the axon). Some specialization of sense organs, notably the statocyst and "eyes" in the form of pigment spots or cups, has occurred in the Acoela. The effector system is still essentially that of a longitudinal and a circular sheet of muscle cells, a "muscle field system." A nerve network can adequately control such a diffuse effector system; however, diffuse nervous control and the lack of mechanical versatility of a "muscle field" preclude the execution of complex movements. As a consequence, complicated and rapid behavior is denied these animals.

In polyclad flatworms, the nervous system has retreated from its exposed position at the surface of the body to form a submuscular plexus. Longitudinal cords are emphasized, the ventral ones becoming strongly developed (Fig. 4-2). These nerve cords, like those of Acoela and Chitons, are not pure fiber tracts; they are mixtures of cell bodies and axons. Accordingly, one part of the cord, and hence, of the animal, is practically as talented as another. This is true even though there is a tendency for the cords to thicken at the anterior end. In the polyclad flatworms, the "brain" attains great complexity (Fig. 4-3), but the word "brain" is misleading here in that it implies too much, behaviorally. The so-called brains are concentrations of cells employed principally to funnel into the nervous system the increased number of fibers arising from the greater multitude of sense organs that are now concentrated at the anterior end of the animal (Figs. 4-4 and 4-5).

Fig. 4-2. Part of the nervous system of a polyclad flatworm. (Redrawn from Hyman.)

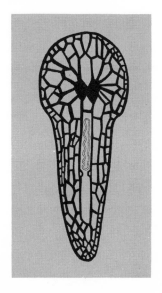

Like the marginal bodies of coelenterates, the "brain" initiates activity that passes down the cords and, in this sense, influences locomotion. As long as a piece of nerve cord is left intact in a fragment of planaria, however, spontaneous movement and some coordinated responses persist. Decapitated flatworms tend to be inactive, not entirely because loss of the anterior ganglion impairs the functioning of the rest of the system, but because the animal is deprived of the sensory information that initiates and regulates much of its behavior. These animals are still very much stimulus-response systems. Their responses to light, currents, and chemicals are stereotyped. Greater accuracy in orienting to the source of a stimulus is exhibited by flatworms than by lower animals, because a greater development of sense organs (Fig. 4-5) permits comparisons of intensities of a stimulus successively (klinotaxis) or simultaneously (tropotaxis).

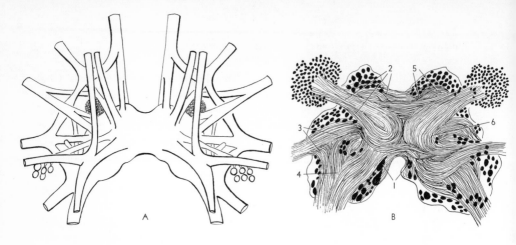

Fig. 4-3. Brain of a polyclad flatworm showing the nerves (A) and (B) various ganglion cells (1) and fiber tracts (2–6) within the central mass. (Redrawn from Hyman, Vol. 2, after Hadenfeldt, 1929.)

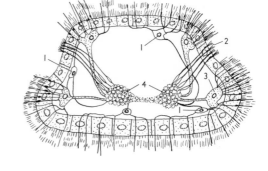

Fig. 4-4. Diagrammatic section through the head of a flatworm showing the brain (4) and the various kinds of receptors: (1) touch receptor, (2) chemoreceptors, (3) rheoreceptors. (Redrawn from Hyman, Vol. 2, after Gelei, 1930.)

Fig. 4-5. An advanced type of eye of a land planarian showing retinal clubs (1), cornea (2), pigment cells (3), and nerve cells of the retinal clubs (4). (Redrawn from Hyman, after Hesse, 1902.)

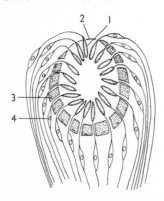

Habituation, the tendency to ignore eventually a stimulus that produces no harmful effects, is common among flatworms. There is also evidence (still controversial) that they can be conditioned to light and to mechanical stimuli and that the anterior end of the animal is not essential for this accomplishment. In other words, the nascent bilateral nervous system, like the radial system, acts not only in accordance with changes impressed upon it at the moment, but is also influenced by what has happened before.

It is clear that the mere concentration of nervous tissue at the front end is insufficient for the performance of complicated behavior. The pioneer possessors

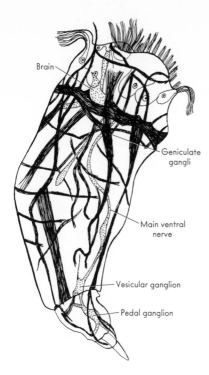

Fig. 4-6. The musculature (shown in heavy shading) and nervous system of a Rotifer. (Redrawn from Hyman, Vol. 3, after Martini, 1912.)

Fig. 4-7. Relations between the terminations of sensory neurons (fs.) and motor neurons (nm.) in the ventral nerve cord of an oligochaete (Pheretima communissima) (fgm., giant fiber). (Redrawn after Ogawa, Sci. Rep. Tokohu Imp. Univ., 13, 1939, 395–488.)

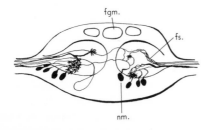

of bilateral systems do not outshine in behavior the most highly developed coelenterates nor even some of the protozoa. The Rotifers, for example, which resemble ciliate protozoa remarkably in size and superficial structure, do not—despite having a "brain," nerve cords, sensory and motor nerves, and a bewildering array of muscles (Fig. 4-6)—appreciably surpass the ciliates in behavior. Nor do the Entoprocta, small sessile metazoans that have nerves, a main nerve mass, and muscles excel the stalked protozoa they so closely resemble. It is the cellular organization within the central mass plus a versatile mechanical system to play upon that counts.

GANGLIA

In the nerve net, it will be recalled, the cells and their processes are more or less evenly scattered in space. As certain processes elongated to the exclusion of others, the bundles of fibers so formed still retained cells within their confines (Fig. 2-3), but as animals evolved, there was an increasing tendency to reserve cords for conducting elements and to gather the cell bodies together into localized masses (ganglia) (Fig. 4-7). Cords, being through-conducting systems, transmitted faster than a net. The ultimate in speed was achieved by the development of giant fibers, which transmitted faster because of their great diameter and which had fewer synaptic connections, and hence fewer delays, than ordinary fibers. These express lines of the central nervous system are found in annelids, molluscs, and arthropods, where they are used in such escape mechanisms as the violent tail-snapping response of lobsters. With these developments, the central nervous system sank deeper into the body, where it became protected with various supporting tissues. In these relatively deep locations, more or less equidistant from sense organs and muscles, it became the center where fibers to and from different parts of the body meet.

The choice of location for ganglia seems to depend on the configuration of the body and the desirability of placing relay stations in regions where great and special activity takes place. As already mentioned, this is pre-eminently the front end, that end of the animal first exposed to the vagaries of the environment, where large numbers of sense organs must be tied into the nervous system. This portion of the central nervous system remains dorsal to the alimentary canal, while the rest of the system is ventral. The two are connected by nerves going around the gut. The greatest development occurs in the dorsal region (supraoesophageal, or cerebral, ganglia) and the next greatest immediately below (suboesophageal ganglia). The degree of development of anterior ganglia is closely correlated with the complexity and mass of sensory equipment. Thus the head ganglia of free-living roundworms are well developed compared with those of parasitic worms, the trematodes and cestodes, whose sense organs are few. Where extensive motor activity is called for, ganglia tend to arise as motor relay stations. The pedal ganglion in the razor clam (*Ensis*) is an example. The anal and genital regions are also sites of ganglion formation (e.g., the peri-anal ganglion of *Ascaris*). The placement of ganglia in strategic locations is most strikingly illustrated by the molluscs, which have at least three pairs: cerebral, pedal, and visceral (Fig. 4-8). Animals that became markedly segmented (annelids and arthropods) initially developed segmentally arranged ganglia (Fig. 4-9).

Fig. 4-8. Molluscan nervous systems. (A) A chiton. (B) A gastropod. (C) A lamellibranch (ce.g., cerebral ganglion; p.v.c., pleurovisceral commissure; pa.g., parietal ganglion; ped.g., pedal ganglion; pl.g., pleural ganglion; vis.g., visceral ganglion). (Redrawn from Borradaile and Potts, Invertebrata. New York: Macmillan, 1935.)

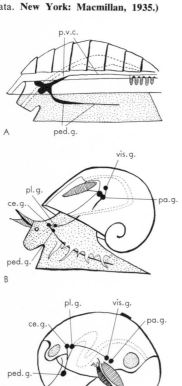

The role of ganglia in relaying sensory activity to effectors and in ordering or coordinating the action of the effectors they serve is most clearly
seen in the locomotor activity of worms. Flatworms, which lack a complicated musculature, are well served by a nerve net and ganglionated cords.
Since the skeletal development of roundworms permitted a highly organized
musculature, intricate modes of movement became possible. The draconematid worm, for example, is able to progress in an inchworm-like fashion
because it is able to coordinate the number and sequence of muscles that
contract (Fig. 4-10). In a segmented animal, even more versatile locomotion is possible. How this is accomplished in the earthworm is illustrated
by the ingenious experiment of Friedlander shown in Fig. 4-11.

The earthworm moves by means of waves of peristalsis passing from
anterior to posterior. If the entire ventral nerve cord is removed, locomotion is not possible. This proves that activity is not propagated by the
subepidermal nerve net. If a worm is transected completely except for the
nerve cord, which is the only part that holds the two ends of the worm
together, a coordinated peristaltic wave still occurs. However, its persist-
ence when the cord is cut or even removed from several segments shows
that it need not be transmitted via the cord. If a completely transected worm

Fig. 4-9. Anterior part of the nervous
system of the earthworm (Lumbricus
terrestris): b., mouth; cb., buccal
cavity; ce., cerebral ganglion; P.,
prostomium; ph., pharynx; sg., stoma-
togastric nervous system; so., suboesophageal ganglion. (Redrawn after
Hess, J. Morph., 40, 1925, 235–261.)

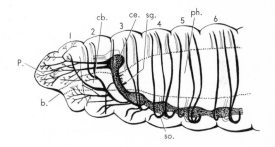

Fig. 4-10. Inchworm-like locomotion of a free-living nematode (draconematid).
(Redrawn from Hyman, after Stauffer, 1924.)

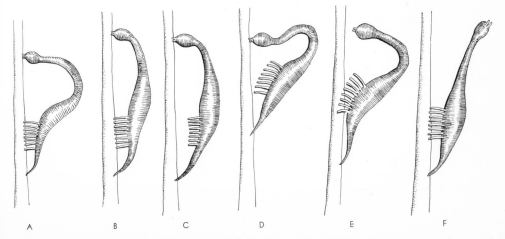

A   B   C   D   E   F

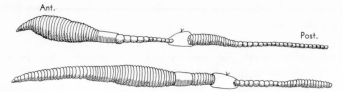

Fig. 4-11. The experiment of Friedlander (1888) demonstrated that a contraction wave would pass from the posterior end to the anterior end of a worm even though a gap of a centimeter separated two halves, provided the halves were joined by a thread. (Redrawn from Grassé, Traité de Zoologie, 5, 1959, 262.)

is held together by threads (Fig. 4-11), the wave is essentially normal. This clever experiment illustrates that as each segment contracts, it exerts traction on the succeeding segment (via the threads) and stimulates its sense organs (proprioceptors), whose activity is relayed to the muscles of that segment by the ganglion. Peristalsis thus proceeds by way of successive segmental reflex actions.

A different type of locomotion occurs in the sea worm *Nereis,* which moves in a wavy snake-like fashion. Here the coordination of muscle contraction is such that the muscles on one side of a segment contract while the corresponding set on the other side relaxes; this action is alternated. Leeches move by an inchworm-like action that requires still more complex coordination; the anterior and posterior suckers alternately attach and disengage in coordination with the contractions of the body musculature. In these forms, an intact cord and the ganglion serving the motor area are necessary, but the cerebral ganglion is not required. Similarly, the cerebral ganglion is not required by the mussel (*Mytilus*) when it moves and spins threads for attachment to the substrate (using the visceral ganglion). Clearly, it is possible for each area of these animals to be more or less autonomous and still act in concert with other parts without a master control center. The potentialities of this arrangement are definitely limited.

Ganglia (and ganglionated cords) act not only as relay stations but also initiate activity. Thus, complicated adaptive movements may be carried on by a series of spontaneously active "clocks." The lugworm (*Arenicola marina*), for example, lives in a U-shaped burrow which it keeps open by rhythmic respiratory, locomotory, and feeding movements. These rhythmic cycles (the defecation cycle, too) are not simple reflexes in response to a changing environment; they are rhythmic muscular contractions driven by spontaneous activity in various parts of the nervous system. The brain is quite unnecessary; isolated fragments of the animal perform their normal cycle well.

BEHAVIOR IN SIMPLE GANGLIONATED INVERTEBRATES

Coincident with the development of complex means of locomotion has been the elaboration of mechanical senses to detect stress and strains within the body and to signal the postural relation of one part of the body to another.

As a consequence, behavior consists not only of locomotion and feeding but also of characteristic postural attitudes (e.g., the positions assumed by earthworms during copulation) and of manipulation of the environment.

Despite the lack of appendages (in earthworms) or anything more than mere fleshy flaps (parapodia of seaworms), a certain dexterity has been attained by worms. Darwin was fascinated by the apparent intelligence earthworms show in dragging leaves into their burrows. Emerging from its burrow at night, an earthworm keeps its posterior end firmly anchored in the gallery as it stretches its anterior end across the surface of the ground in exploratory movement. When certain vegetable debris is encountered, it is pulled over and into the burrow by the proboscis. Darwin believed that leaves (or bits of paper cut into various shapes) were always seized in such a way as to insure that the shape offered the least resistance to passage into the burrow. Although it is true that the worm can differentiate the stem from the other end of a leaf by chemical stimuli, recent studies have shown that the successful pulling of leaves into a burrow is a trial-and-error process. By and large the actions of earthworms are simple, rigid responses to stimuli.

Many aquatic worms construct quite serviceable tubes in which they live. One such (*Aulophorus carteri*) builds a tube with the spores of an aquatic plant (Fig. 4-12). The anterior end of the worm undulates until the prostomium encounters a spore. When this happens, the head is flexed and the spore is taken into the mouth and covered with saliva. The worm then retracts to bring the spore to the top of the tube, where it is held in place until firmly stuck.

Some sea worms (e.g., *Chaetopterus*) secrete mucus that is manipulated to form a bag which serves as a strainer for removing food from water circulated through it. When the bag is full, it is rolled up, transferred to the mouth, and swallowed.

At this level of neural organization, animals can not only become habituated but can also be conditioned fairly readily, especially to light, touch, and electrical shock. In worms, the brain is not required. Whether higher levels of learning are possible is questionable. The behavior of worms in a simple T-maze suggests that it is; however, the experiments require confirmation. Some snails, however, clearly learn T-mazes.

Fig. 4-12. Method of tube construction by the worm Aulophorus Carteri, using the spores of an aquatic plant. (Redrawn after Carter and Beadle, 1931, from Grassé, Traité de Zoologie, 5, 1959, 390.)

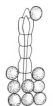 

HIERARCHY OF CONTROL AND CEPHALIZATION

As the nervous system condensed in the course of evolution from a diffuse net, it was no longer functionally similar throughout. The increasing importance of ganglia in controlling those areas of the body that they innervate finally demanded that they themselves come under some higher control; otherwise the animal would have to act like a republic of parts rather than as a unit, and chaos would prevail. The role of master control center fell to the anterior ganglia, especially the supraoesophageal (cerebral) one.

Originally, cerebral ganglia were principally sensory relay centers (Fig. 4-7). Oligochaete worms (earthworms), for example, can still eat and burrow in normal fashion after removal of the cerebral ganglia. The simplest type of control that cerebral ganglia exercised was that of excitation and inhibition of other ganglia. In polychaete worms, the head ganglia (Fig. 4-13) are more than relay stations. The supraoesophageal one is an inhibitory center; the suboesophageal one, a motor center. Without the former, *Nereis* no longer feeds or burrows, is less sensitive to light and chemicals and is hyperactive. Without the suboesophageal ganglion, it is inactive (akinetic).

In Gastropod molluscs (snails, limpets, etc.), the cerebral (supraoesophageal) ganglion has clearly become the controlling center for the activities of the animal. As a consequence of its development, these animals are capable of behavior of considerable complexity. In addition to habituation and simple conditioning, they exhibit complicated coordinated reflex behavior and a marked ability to modify their behavior. The snail *Helix,* for instance, displays a complicated courtship behavior in which two individuals approach, evert their genital areas, and launch calcareous darts with enough force to penetrate each other's internal organs. Following this heroic stimulation, fertilization takes place.

Fig. 4-13. Cerebral ganglia in a polychaete worm (Nereis diversicolor): **An., antenna; Na., antennal nerve; Ca., Cp., perioesophageal commissures; P., palp; Np., palpal nerve; Pd., portion of pedunculate body; Oa., Op., eyes.** (Redrawn after Retzius, Biol. Untersuch., **7, 1895, 6–11.**)

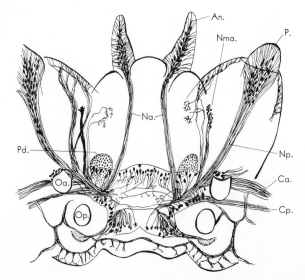

Some snails learn a T-maze after 60 trials and retain the habit for about 30 days. Other gastropods, notably limpets, show a homing sense that suggests true learning of topographic relations. Limpets, which fasten themselves to a particular spot on a rock and make feeding excursions from there at low tide, usually return to the same spot. Although they may return along the outgoing path, they are not dependent on it and may return from a distance as great as five feet by an entirely different route. This behavior would tend to rule out the use of trail-following cues. It indicates that these animals can make a well-integrated assessment of sensory cues.

INTEGRATION AND COMPARTMENTALIZATION

Ganglia began as relay stations. Later they started to modify the messages they received before passing them on to motor systems. They also began to initiate activity, which they passed on. They acquired these accomplishments when they ceased to be mere aggregations of sensory and motor cell bodies whose axons stretch out to the farthest reaches of the body. Indeed, many new cells were added whose processes never extend beyond the confines of the ganglion. Ganglion development was characterized by multiplicity and complexity. Not only was the number of neurons increased, the kinds of neurons increased. An infinite number of varieties differing in size, shape, and number of processes, in shape and size of cell body, and in the number and nature of connections arose. Differences in structure reflect differences in function. And the cells of ganglia then gathered together into tight groups, which enhanced the number of possible connections in a given space and reduced the time of transmission.

As ganglia became compartmentalized, function became localized in different areas, ganglia became integrative centers of great complexity, and behavior extended to new horizons. One need only compare the simple ventral ganglion of an oligochaete worm (Fig. 4-7), the elementary cerebral ganglia of a polyclad flatworm (Fig. 4-3) and those of one of the chordate ancestors of

Fig. 4-14. Transverse section through the cerebral ganglion of the ascidian Phallusia nigra, showing the concentration of ganglion cell bodies in the cortical region. (Redrawn from Hilton, J. Ent. Zool. Claremont, **33**, 1941, 44–53.)

the vertebrates (Fig. 4-14), the more complex ganglion of a polychaete worm (Fig. 4-13), of the insect (Fig. 4-17), and of the vertebrate (Fig. 5-1) to appreciate the significance these developments must have had on behavior. And in our preoccupation with neurons, we must not overlook a significant new development, beginning in annelids: the incorporation into ganglia of cells (neurosecretory) whose secretions have profound effects on the behavior of animals.

CEPHALOPODS (SQUIDS, CUTTLEFISH, OCTOPUSES)

Cephalopods have the largest brains of all invertebrates. The supraesophageal ganglia have burgeoned forth and, in association with the subesophageal ganglia, form a complex and highly talented brain composed of, in the case of the octopus, about 168×10^6 cells. As a consequence of this development, Cephalopods are capable of behavior that far outstrips that of any of their evolutionary predecessors. They exhibit complicated postural and fright behavior, sexual display (in *Sepia*), and intricate copulation behavior. The octopus, for example, inserts one arm into the mantle cavity of the female and deposits a spermatophore there. The octopus constructs a home from debris on the ocean floor; it has territorial behavior, that is, it confines its activities to a circumscribed area and behaves aggressively toward other individuals entering this area; it has visual discrimination and form perception equal to or exceeding that of insects; it can be conditioned readily and learns a maze with ease. Its learning abilities greatly transcend those of any animal we have encountered thus far. It is capable both of visual learning and of tactile learning, and it is one of the few invertebrates with arms for grasping and manipulating. Nevertheless, octopuses never learn to make skilled movements, and they do not behave as elaborately as might be expected from their sensory and motor equipment.

All these advances in behavior, and the limits as well, are indisputably associated with the development of the brain. The contributions of different parts of the brain to behavior have been studied by electrical stimulation and by lesions. They clearly demonstrate great subdivision of function. Complexity, multiplicity, and compartmentalization have been carried to the

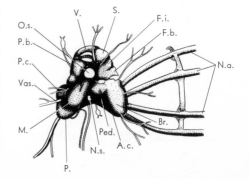

Fig. 4-15. The brain of Octopus, dissected out and seen from the right side, with the optic stalk cut and the optic lobe removed. O.s., = optic stalk; P.b., posterior basal; P. c., posterior chromatophore; Vas., vasomotor; M., magnocellular; P., palliovisceral; Ped., pedal; N.s., nerves to the statocyst; A.c., anterior chromatophore; Br., brachial; N.a., nerves to the arms; F.b., frontal buccal; F.i., frontal interior; S., superior; V., vertical. (From M. J. Wells, Brain and Behaviour in Cephalopods, p. 93. Stanford: Stanford University Press, 1962.)

point where there are fourteen main lobes mediating different functions (Fig. 4-15). The anatomically lower lobes regulate only simple functions; the sensory lobes (e.g., optic lobes) receive, discriminate, and analyze stimuli from the environment and appropriately activate the motor centers; the highest centers (anatomically and functionally) get activity from sensory ones, mediate complex behavior, and monitor and regulate the entire system.

We can investigate the contributions of the various centers to behavior by making cuts and lesions in various parts of the brain. An octopus with only its suboesophageal lobes (Fig. 4-16A) is like a spinal vertebrate (one in which only the spinal cord is functional) in that it is capable only of simple reflex movements. If these lower motor centers retain their con-

Fig. 4-16. Diagram illustrating the effect of removal of various parts of the brain on the posture and movements of the octopus. (A) Complete removal of supraoesophageal lobes. (B) Complete removal of supraoesophageal lobes leaving optico-suboesophageal connections intact. (C) Severance of optic tracts and removal of half of the supraoesophageal ganglia. (Redrawn from Boycott and Young, "Physiological Mechanisms in Animal Behavior," Symposia, Soc. Exp. Biol., IV, New York: Academic Press, 1950.)

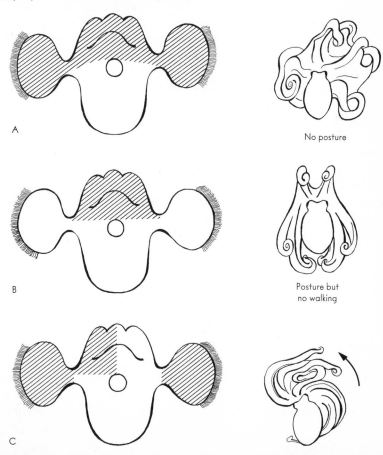

A

No posture

B

Posture but no walking

C

nections with sensory lobes (e.g., optic ones) but are isolated from the rest of the brain (Fig. 4-16B), the animal maintains a rigid posture much like that of a decerebrate vertebrate (one with part of the brain removed). With the lower centers plus the optic lobes plus one-half of the supraoesophageal lobes (Fig. 4-16C), the animal can walk, but only in circles.

Compartmentalization of function is carried to a fine degree. Within the supraoesophageal area of the brain, the basal lobes are higher motor centers that may be likened to the midbrain of vertebrates. They produce complex movements of the head and arms, inspiration, etc. Lying above these are five centers that are concerned with still more complex nuances of behavior and with learning. One of these (the vertical) is analogous in many respects with the cerebral cortex of mammals.

The learning ability of the octopus is illustrated by the following example in which an animal was trained to discriminate the presence of a white card signifying shock. At first, the octopus was trained to come forward from its rocky nest in an aquarium to seize a crab that was lowered into the far end of the water by a thread. Then on half the trials, a white card was lowered with the crab, and in these trials, the octopus was driven away from the crab by strong electric shock. After 12 trials, the octopus began to inhibit its approach to the card and by 24 trials consistently remained in its nest when the card was present and consistently came out to feed when the crab was presented alone. The octopus could also learn more difficult problems, in which two cards were used, a small one associated with feeding and a large one associated with electric shock. Also, discriminations of various shapes have been demonstrated in a similar manner. It is interesting, however, that the octopus was rather poor in problems requiring it to "detour" around a barrier. Thus, when a glass partition was lowered between the crab and an octopus, the octopus persisted in swimming straight into the glass and failed to swim around it through an open space.

Visual learning depends on the optic, superiorfrontal, and vertical lobes; tactile learning on the superiorfrontal-subfrontal-vertical lobe system. The vertical lobe is in part a memory system (see p. 96). When it is removed, animals that have been trained to do a task have to be retrained. This lobe is also presumed to distribute to all parts of the optic lobes the representations of visual stimulus patterns being learned.

CRUSTACEA

With the exception of Cephalopods and insects, the Crustacea exhibit a more varied repertoire of behavior than any other invertebrate. Predatory species stalk, ambush, and chase prey. One vegetarian species climbs pandanus trees for fruit which it may then carry to a hiding place. Most Crustaceans carefully and thoroughly groom themselves. Many select shelters to which they return, while others build shelters or dig burrows, plugging up the entrances. Species such as fiddler crabs have a homing sense and a sense of territoriality. Their courtship may be elaborate. There are a number of defense patterns: Some species run, then stop and try to defend themselves; one species holds sea anemones in its claws and points them toward an attacker; many species have elaborate camouflage behavior as, for example, the fiddler crab which plucks sea anemones and by a variety of acrobatic movements plants them on the shell it inhabits. Various degrees of brood care are observed and also different levels of social behavior. Fiddler crabs, for instance, have organized communal feeding groups, familial groups with dominant males, and a ceremonial and fixed pattern of fighting among males. Peck orders are established in these species. Association learning has been demonstrated.

The central nervous system is characterized by a small number of cells (97,722 in the crayfish) and elaborate interneurons that fulfill the function of whole tracts in vertebrates. Most of the behavior can be explained in terms of reflexes—e.g., eyestalk withdrawal, claw closing and opening, escape, defense, feeding, and copulation (both of which are shut off by the brain), and righting.

INSECTS

The apogee of invertebrate behavior is realized in the insects, especially in the Hymenoptera (ants, bees, and wasps). There are over a million species in the Class, and one would hardly expect either the kind or the level of behavior to be uniform in the group. Consequently, we shall examine only the highest behavioral achievements, which illustrate what can be done with the kind of nervous equipment available, and we shall also analyze the relation between behavior and the neural developments we have been discussing.

It is clear from the mountain of literature on the subject that extraordinarily complex behavior is possible. Much of this behavior resembles and even rivals that of mammals, so much so that writers have been led to impute to insects reasoning and intelligence. This is the greatest tribute to the complexity of their behavior; however, experimental analyses show that these are largely stimulus-bound animals that operate in a stereotyped fashion in strict accordance with the stimuli received. At the same time, it must be emphasized that in the higher forms there is a certain plasticity of behavior and that learning attains an important level.

Three developments have made such complicated behavior possible: the elaboration of very complex sense organs, which permit a highly discriminative assessment of the environment; the evolution of jointed appendages and their subsequent modification into legs and mouthparts of extraordinary complexity, making possible an exceptional manipulative ability; the development of a brain that is complex enough and has a sufficiently integrative capacity to organize the wealth of sensory information received and to direct all the motions of the appendages (Fig. 4-17).

The visual, olfactory, and tactile senses have become well developed. The compound eye, the best visual system developed by the invertebrates (with the possible exception of the cephalopod eye), may be deficient in visual acuity, form perception, and color vision by vertebrate standards, but it still possesses these qualities to some extent. It is superior in the perception of flicker, an attribute of considerable adaptive value because of the speed with which many insects fly. The olfactory sense, at least insofar as acuity is concerned, rivals the best that vertebrates have to offer. The mechanical senses are well developed, the proprioceptive senses necessarily so in order to keep the nervous system informed about the positions of the many parts of the highly articulated body; the tactile sense is developed to a degree that makes a highly accurate sensory survey of the substrate possible.

Equipped with these systems, insects are able to manipulate their environment and to maintain elaborate relations with one another. They build nests of great complexity; burrowing bees and wasps hollow out underground nests and provision them with paralyzed prey as food for the young; mud-daubing wasps construct characteristic nests of mud which are also provisioned with prey; paper-building wasps erect elaborate nests from reconstituted wood fiber; honeybees construct precise waxen combs. In rare cases, insects use a bit of the environment as a tool. The classical case is that of certain tropical ants that make nests of leaves held together by silken threads. The ants themselves cannot spin, but the larvae can. The adults hold the larvae in their jaws and use them as shuttles.

Coincident with nest building is intimate association with others of the species. These associations culminate in highly organized social units, a strong sense of territoriality, and the acquisition of considerable homing abilities. Social insects—ants, for example—have morphologically dis-

Fig. 4-17. Simplified diagram of the main areas of the insect brain and their principal fiber tracts: Op.Nv., optic nerve; Op.L., optic lobe; Op.T., optic tract; Cc., corpus centrale; Cpd., corpus pedunculatum or mushroom body; Pncr., pons cerebralis; Picr., pars intercerebralis; Pcr.L., protocerebral lobe; Ac.L., accessory lobe; Ant.Nv., antennal nerve; Ant.C., antennal center; 1 Com., 2 Com., 3 Com., commissures; Fr.Gng., frontal ganglion; Coe.Con., circumoesphageal connectives to suboesophageal ganglion. (Redrawn from Snodgrass, Principles of Insect Morphology. New York: McGraw-Hill, 1935.)

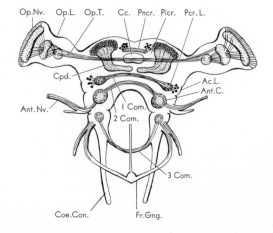

tinct castes, each of which has its own characteristic behavior. This fact is especially interesting, since all may be of the same genotype. The activities of the specialized castes may be quite bizarre, ranging from hunting, defense of the colony, and capturing and enslavement of other species, to cultivation of fungus gardens, care and tending of aphids (whose saccharine secretions are highly prized), and conversion of themselves into veritable wine casks for the storage of honey for the needs of the colony.

Territoriality involves the defense of a given piece of ground, the recognition of home, and the ability to orient to it from a distance. Insects' powers of orientation and their ability to learn and remember landmarks rival that of the mammals. Walking forms (ants) deposit and follow chemical trails or orient by visual cues and the polarized light pattern of daylight. Flying forms (bees, wasps) orient by visual landmarks and can navigate over distances as great as a mile by determining the position of the sun and the plane of polarization of the light in the sky. Experiments in which landmarks have been moved proved that new landmarks can be learned very quickly, in one nine-second orientation flight. Honeybees carry this ability further; in the hive they perform dances whose speed and orientation with respect to gravity code the distance and direction from the hive to a given supply of food.

The wide scope of these activities leads the unwary to postulate a higher behavioral capacity than these insects actually possess. It goes without saying that habituation is a common phenomenon. Indeed, integrated social behavior can be largely explained by habituation. For example, strangers in an ant or bee nest are immediately recognized on the basis of their odor and are often killed. If, however, a stranger is introduced at a time when the colony is busy with other matters, he may pass unnoticed and eventually be accepted. One explanation is that the others become habituated to his odor.

Innate responses to stimuli also explain much of the highly organized behavior of the social insects. For instance, performance and interpretation of the intricate bee dance are not learned. Time sense is built into such insects as bees as part of the same endogenous clock system that regulates periodic activities in many animals. In navigation, the automatic correlation between the sun's position, the plane of polarization, and the pull of gravity (when the dance is being done) is innate. On the other hand, visual cues in the environment are learned.

The learning ability of insects varies greatly from one species to the next. Most insects are capable of classical conditioning; they can be made to associate an adverse stimulus such as electric shock with light, dark, etc. Certain insects can be instrumentally conditioned. Bees can be trained to associate food with a given color or shape. Ants exhibit considerable proficiency in learning a maze (Fig. 4-18).

Although learning is an important component of behavior in many

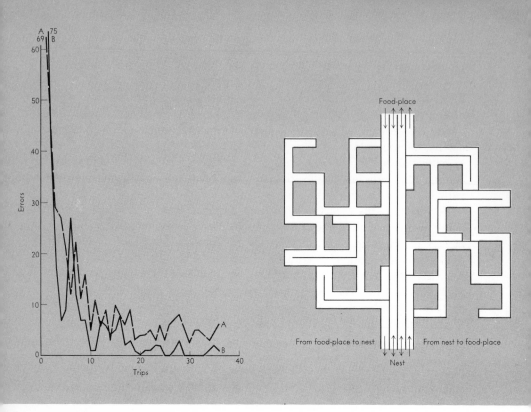

Fig. 4-18. (Left) Learning curve for a fairly successful performance of Formica incerta in the maze shown at right. A is outward trip to food place. B is return trip to nest. (Right) Maze used by Schneirla (1933) in the investigation of ant learning. (Redrawn from Thorpe, Learning and Instinct in Animals. Cambridge: Harvard University Press, 1956, after Schneirla, 1933.)

ants, bees, and wasps, for insects as a class it plays a relatively minor role. Insect behavior may be complicated and may mimic many aspects of the behavior of vertebrates, but insects are still stimulus-bound, reflex animals. Their behavior probably represents the farthest development possible in reflex behavior. Higher learning requires further extension of the principles of multiplicity and complexity, which in turn require additional integrative units in the brain. In this endeavor, insects are defeated by their small size.

The
Vertebrate
Nervous System

Turning now to the vertebrates, we come upon a new specialization in the evolutionary development of the nervous system, for these animals with backbones have a single, hollow, dorsal nerve cord that terminates anteriorly in a large ganglionic mass, the brain. The trends seen in the invertebrates continue in the vertebrates, for there is a further central concentration of neural tissue and an enlargement of the over-all size of the central nervous system, owing to an increase in both the number of nerve cells and the complexity and extensiveness of their interconnections. Most important of all, however, is the continued process of *encephalization*—the great expansion in size and functional capacities of the more anterior parts of the central nervous system, in short, the great development of the brain itself.

The striking nature of these changes can readily be seen upon gross examination of representative vertebrate brains (Fig. 5-1). Two points are noteworthy here. First, among the vertebrates, brain-weights range from a few grams in fish, amphibia, and even large reptiles to 1200–1400 grams in man, and even more in large animals like the elephant and whale. Second, there is a progressive change in the configuration of the brain, as we can see in the enormous development of the cerebral hemispheres and particularly in the cortex overlying them. In order to appreciate the full significance of the process of encephalization, it will be helpful to review briefly the structure and function of the major subdivisions of the brain and of the spinal cord leading into it.

By taking up the spinal cord first, we shall have a chance to see the organization of a relatively simple part of the central nervous system that has perhaps undergone the least change in phylogeny, and, at the same time, we shall learn something of the plan of the central nervous system. Then we can consider the major subdivisions of the brain itself and see how the great changes in behavioral capacities from fish to mammals, including man, can be related to the morphological changes in the nervous system that occur in encephalization.

THE SPINAL CORD

In all vertebrates, the spinal cord has two major functions. One is the *integration of reflex behavior* occurring in the trunk and limbs, and the other is the *conduction* of nervous impulses to and from the brain. A reflex is a simple response to a simple stimulus such as the knee jerk or the withdrawal of a limb to painful stimulation. The basic spinal mechanism for integrating reflexes is the *reflex arc* (Fig. 5-2). Typically, it consists of the following components: (1) *receptors* in the skin, muscles, and

Fig. 5-1. Lateral views of representative vertebrate brains: (A) codfish, (B) frog, (C) alligator, (D) goose, (E) horse, (F) man. (C., cerebrum; Ce., cerebellum; D., diencephalon; E., epiphysis; F.lo., frontal lobe; I.lo., inferior lobe; In., infundibulum; M., medulla; Oc.lo., occipital lobe; Ol.b., olfactory bulb; Ol.lo., olfactory lobe; O.lo., optic lobe; Ol.t., olfactory tract; O.t., optic tract; P., pituitary; Pa.lo., parietal lobe; P.lo., piriform lobe; Po., pons; R.f., rhinal fissure; T.lo., temporal lobe.) (After Romer.)

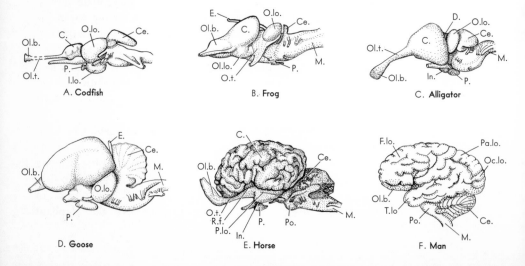

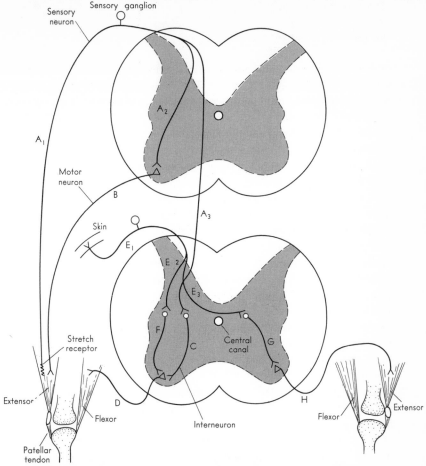

Fig. 5-2. Schematic diagram of two adjacent segments of the spinal cord, showing examples of connections of sensory neurons, interneurons, and motor neurons, making up various reflex arcs.

The monosynaptic arc involved in the knee jerk is activated when the extensor
muscle is stretched by the patellar tap. This involves sensory neuron A_1 leading
from the stretch receptor through its central branch A_2 to the motor neuron B
which activates contractions in the extensor, lifting the leg. At the same time,
there is reciprocal inhibition of the antagonistic flexor muscles, probably through
the polysynaptic arc, involving another branch of the sensory neuron A_3 and
the interneuron C, resulting in inhibition of the motor neuron D and relaxation
of the flexors.

The polysynaptic arc in the withdrawal reflex to painful stimulation of the
skin on the distal part of a leg involves sensory neuron E_1 and its central branch
E_2, interneuron F, and the excitation of motor neuron D, leading to a contraction of the flexors.

At the same time, a crossed-extension reflex occurs over another branch of
the sensory neuron, E_3, through the interneuron G and the motor neuron H,
resulting in excitation of the extensor muscles on the opposite side. Not shown
in these last two cases are the reciprocal inhibitory influences on the muscles
antagonistic to those contracting and the feedback from the stretch receptors
that are present in all the muscles. Also, it should be pointed out that while only
one neuron is portrayed in each component of the reflex arc, actually many, many
neurons typically work in concert. (Modified from D. P. C. Lloyd, "Synaptic Mechanisms," in J. F. Fulton, ed., A Textbook of Physiology. Philadelphia: Saunders,
1955.)

joints that are selectively sensitive to various stimuli and form the beginning of (2) *afferent* or *sensory nerves,* or *neurons,* that enter the dorsal part of the spinal cord and terminate in contact with (3) *interneurons,* or *associational neurons,* that in turn terminate upon (4) *efferent,* or *motor, neurons* that pass out of the ventral part of the cord to end in appropriate *effectors,* either muscles or glands (Fig. 5-2).

In some cases like the knee jerk, the sensory neurons connect directly with the motor neurons in a *monosynaptic arc* reminiscent of the direct sensory-motor connections found in the simpler invertebrates. As a rule, however, it is through the many connections of the associational neurons within the spinal cord that information coming over various sensory neurons is organized and integrated so that a pattern of activity is set up in the motor neurons, leading to an organized pattern of response. This response is a spinal reflex such as that seen in the withdrawal or flexion of a limb when a noxious or painful stimulus is applied to its distal end. While such a reflex looks simple, it is actually a complex, patterned response, requiring the integrated action of many muscles and involving a number of basic neurophysiological mechanisms. For example, in order to execute a *flexion reflex,* an organism must contract its flexor muscles, which pull the limb toward the body, and simultaneously relax the antagonistic extensor muscles. This pattern of stopping an activity when its antagonist is started is the classical pattern of *reciprocal excitation* and *inhibition* that we will see many times in the study of the nervous system. At the same time that one limb is flexed, it may be necessary for the animal to extend its opposite limb for support against the ground in a *crossed-extension reflex* which calls for a contraction of extensor muscles and a relaxation of flexors. Together these two reflexes make up the basic pattern of stepping.

In all these actions, the contracting muscles may actually stretch the opposing relaxing muscles. Whenever muscles are stretched by the action of their antagonists, stretch receptors embedded in the muscles are activated, and a *stretch reflex* is initiated. In this reflex, the stretched muscles begin to contract and the antagonistic muscles begin to relax, offsetting the original reflex somewhat. In addition, the stretch reflex activates special small motor neurons that go back to the very same stretch receptors, and their action there may result in a reduction of the stretch imposed on the receptors so that they are "reset" to an optimal range of sensitivity. Then they can more readily respond to still further stretch that may be imposed upon them. The net effect of all these neurophysiological mechanisms is to permit movements to be executed in a smooth and graded fashion, sensitively integrated into a meaningful whole with all other movements.

All these reflexes may be obtained in the spinal animal where the spinal cord is severed from the brain, and indeed the basic integrating mechanisms may be contained within a few segments of the spinal cord. So it is easy to see, in even a simple system, what an important role the central nervous system may play in the sorting of sensory information and in the organization and patterning of motor responses. More complex reflex functions like the *scratch reflex* and *walking reflexes* require the organization of even more sensory information over many segments of the spinal cord and the coordination of even more complex patterns of response.

In addition to mediating skeletal muscle reflexes, the spinal cord is connected, through special nerves branching off from it, to the *autonomic nervous system* which innervates the viscera, blood vessels, and other smooth musculature of the body. As you can see in Fig. 5-3, the *sympa-*

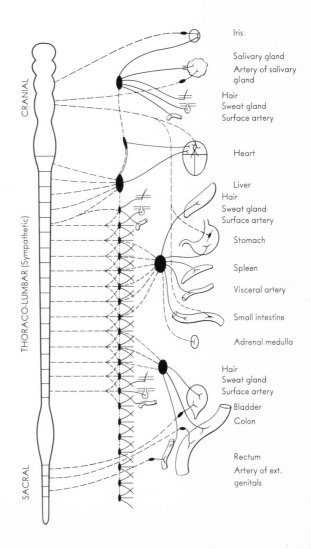

Fig. 5-3. Diagram of the brain and spinal cord (left), showing the sympathetic ganglionic chain in the thoracic-lumbar region of the cord and the parasympathetic outflow from the brain and the sacral region of the cord. (Redrawn from W. B. Cannon, The Wisdom of the Body. **New York: Norton, 1932.)**

CRANIAL

THORACO-LUMBAR (Sympathetic)

SACRAL

Iris

Salivary gland
Artery of salivary gland

Hair
Sweat gland
Surface artery

Heart

Liver
Hair
Sweat gland
Surface artery

Stomach

Spleen

Visceral artery

Small intestine

Adrenal medulla

Hair
Sweat gland
Surface artery

Bladder
Colon

Rectum
Artery of ext. genitals

thetic branch of the peripheral autonomic nervous system, lying along the middle region of the cord, consists of a chain of ganglia which sends out a diffuse network of fibers to the organs innervated. From the hindmost region of the cord and from the brain arise the nerve fibers of the *parasympathetic branch* of the autonomic nervous system; these fibers go directly to the individual organs they innervate over discrete, individual pathways. In general, the sympathetic system functions in active processes that expend energy (increased heart rate, blood pressure, pupil dilation, etc.) and the parasympathetic functions in repair (promotes digestion, sleep, etc.), but this "antagonism" is not always distinct or consistent. Both systems have their central representation in the various parts of the brain concerned with visceral functions (medulla, hypothalamus, old cortex).

When the influence of the brain on spinal reflex mechanisms is intact, the complexity of reflexes and other behavior increases vastly. This is achieved by nervous conduction to and from the brain through long columns or tracts of nerve fibers (axons) that run up and down the peripheral parts of the spinal cord. Upon gross examination, the columns appear white (Fig. 5-2), for the larger axons in them are sheathed in a white fatty substance called myelin. The butterfly-shaped core of the spinal cord is gray, for it consists mainly of cell bodies of associational and motor neurons that are unmyelinated. The *ascending,* or *sensory, columns* consist mainly of long branches of peripheral sensory neurons coming into the spinal cord and crossing to the opposite side early in their central course (Fig. 5-4). In a large animal, these individual nerve cells may thus be many feet in length, especially in the case of peripheral nerves arising in the foot and going up into the brain. To a large degree, different sensory systems are segregated within the spinal cord so that there are somewhat separate columns mediating pain, temperature sense, muscle sense (or proprioception), and touch. The *descending,* or *motor, columns* consist of neurons going all the way down from the brain and crossing to the motor nerve cells in the ventral parts of the spinal cord (Fig. 5-4). Because of this crossing in both the motor and sensory neurons, the left side of the brain typically controls the right side of the body and vice versa, so that with a brain injury, there is usually paralysis or loss of sensitivity on the opposite side of the body.

In the course of vertebrate phylogeny, the basic organization of the spinal cord undergoes relatively little change. As the forward parts of the brain develop, however, the ascending spinal columns extend up to them (thalamus), and the descending columns originate in the highest parts of the cerebrum, the cortex itself. At the same time, the tracts become more concentrated and distinct and their functional connections more discrete, all of which permits greater refinement and segregation of functions.

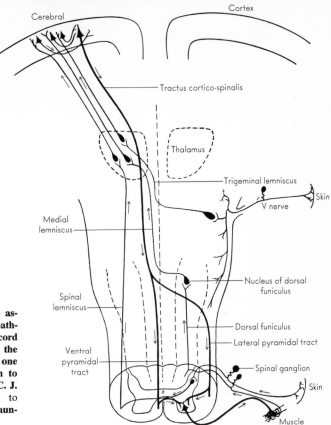

Cortex

Cerebral

Tractus cortico-spinalis

Thalamus

Trigeminal lemniscus

Skin

V nerve

Medial lemniscus

Nucleus of dorsal funiculus

Spinal lemniscus

Dorsal funiculus

Lateral pyramidal tract

Ventral pyramidal tract

Spinal ganglion

Skin

Muscle

Fig. 5-4. Diagram of the ascending and descending pathways between the spinal cord and the brain, showing the crossing of pathways from one side of the nervous system to the other. (Redrawn from C. J. Herrick, An Introduction to Neurology. **Philadelphia: Saunders, 1931.)**

In this discussion of the spinal cord, we have illustrated, in somewhat simple form, some of the basic principles of organization and function that apply to the vertebrate nervous system as a whole. First, as was illustrated in the reflex arc, we can see that the nervous system, with its sensory, associational, and motor components, is a great stimulus-response correlation mechanism. Second, it operates according to a principle of reciprocal excitation and inhibition, so that as one activity is started, another, perhaps antagonistic, activity is actively stopped. Third, it has built into it a feedback mechanism from the muscles so that it is promptly influenced by the consequences of its own activities. Fourth, in addition to such sensory monitoring of motor activities, there is also a motor or efferent modulation of sensory activity, as in the case of "resetting" the stretch receptor.

As we turn to the complexities of the brain itself, we shall see additional principles of nervous action illustrated, for the brain has additional associational mechanisms for the integration of sensory and motor activities over its own neurons, or through the ascending and descending columns, over the spinal neurons. Thus, in the case of man, for example, a painful stimulus in the toe results automatically in a spinal reflex of withdrawal; in addition, however, the information is integrated at several levels within the brain, a sensation and perhaps an emotion result, and the reflex may be modified or inhibited in the light of other information reaching the brain—by attitudes, past experiences, etc. Not only is the reflex behavior mediated through the vertebrate brain likely to be more complex and variable than spinal reflexes, but, as we shall see, additional behavioral properties appear as a result of the enormously complex network of associational neurons as well as of the specialized sensory and motor mechanisms of the brain.

THE BRAIN

The brain itself may be divided into three major regions—the forebrain, the midbrain, and the hindbrain—that appear early in the embryonic development of all vertebrates as three primary vesicles, or swellings, in the anterior end of the neural tube. As Fig. 5-5 shows, each of these three regions of the brain further subdivides so that the typical vertebrate brain has five divisions in adulthood; each division has its own specialized structures, and each structure makes its own contribution to

Fig. 5-5. Development of the main divisions of the vertebrate brain from the three primary embryonic vesicles; the forebrain (prosencephalon), midbrain (mesencephalon), and hindbrain (rhombencephalon). (After Romer.)

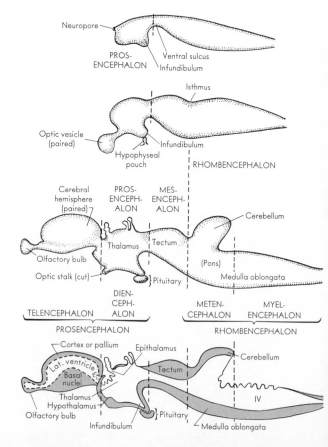

function. As we examine the changes that occur in the evolution of the vertebrate brain, a number of points should be kept in mind.

1. Like the spinal cord, the brain may be divided into sensory and motor structures with great association areas in between.

2. To a large degree, the major evolutionary developments of the brain were occasioned by the development of special receptors whose nerve fibers terminated in different parts of the primitive brain. As the receptors for posture, balance, and equilibrium became more important, a special area in the hindbrain enlarged, becoming the cerebellum. The dorsal part of the midbrain, which was the original terminus of the visual pathways, greatly increased in size as the visual receptors developed. Finally, the cerebral cortex of the forebrain appeared first as the region of the brain mediating olfactory functions.

3. As the more anterior parts of the brain developed and enlarged, they mediated functions once carried out solely by posterior structures. The result is that a given class of functions in an advanced vertebrate may be carried out at several levels of the brain, the anterior levels mediating the more complicated and more recently evolved of these functions and the posterior levels the simpler and more stereotyped.

4. Not all the changes we can trace in vertebrate phylogeny, however, are simple linear increases in the size and functional importance of given structures, for many of the living animals we examine are highly specialized with highly specific adaptations in structure and function. For example, in certain fish that have taste receptors all over the body (catfish), there is enormous development of the vagal lobes of the medulla, where the vagus and other taste nerves have their cell bodies. In mammals, however, where the taste receptors are confined to the tongue, these regions of the medulla are relatively small. With these points in mind, we can now examine the five major divisions of the brain.

MYELENCEPHALON. The hindmost part of the brain, consisting of the *medulla,* is essentially an extension of the spinal cord into the brain, for it contains the continuation of the sensory and motor columns of the cord. In addition, like the cord, it has its own dorsal and its own ventral sensory and motor nerves entering and leaving it; these are the cranial nerves that serve the skin and muscles of the head and the special sense organs concerned with taste, hearing, and balance. Throughout the vertebrates, the medulla functions in the control of vegetative functions, particularly respiratory and cardiovascular ones, but in higher vertebrates, many of these functions are overshadowed by the development of vegetative functions in the hypothalamus and the older parts of the cerebral cortex.

METENCEPHALON. The most prominent structure in this anterior region of the hindbrain is the *cerebellum,* a complex structure serving in the coordination of movements and the maintenance of posture, tone, and bodily equilibrium. In early vertebrates, the cerebellum developed as an enlargement of the vestibular and lateral line centers and received sensory fibers from the muscles (proprioception). Later, new parts of the cerebellum, the cerebellar hemispheres, developed and they received fibers from all the sensory systems.

MESENCEPHALON. This is the midbrain. Its dorsal sensory centers, making up the *tectum,* developed originally in association with optic fibers coming into this region of the brain and became the primary visual center, the large optic lobe, in fish and amphibia. As visual centers in the thalamus and cortex developed ahead of it, the midbrain tectal region, now differentiated as the *superior colliculus,* remained a center for simpler visual functions, off the mainstream of pathways going from the eye to the thalamus and cortex. At the same time, just behind the superior colliculus, the *inferior colliculus* developed as one of several auditory centers relaying to the thalamus and cortex. The lateral and ventral parts of the midbrain, the *tegmentum,* contain the main ascending and descending columns and in addition have local motor reflex mechanisms.

DIENCEPHALON. Within this division of the forebrain are located the *thalamus* in the dorsal region and the *hypothalamus* beneath it. Ahead of the hypothalamus is the entrance and crossing point of the *optic nerves,* and below it is the *pituitary gland.* The dorsal part of the thalamus is the termination point of many of the ascending columns arising in the spinal cord and medulla and, as such, is the great sensory integration mechanism in the lower vertebrates. As the cerebrum develops, certain parts of the thalamus become intimately connected with the sensory regions of the new parts of the cortex and relay information to them. The hypothalamus, as we have already mentioned, has vegetative functions and is concerned with the control of body temperature, sleep, feeding, water balance and drinking, emotion, and reproductive behavior. Also, it exerts neural and humoral control over the pituitary gland, which, besides its own endocrine functions, controls the functions of other endocrine glands of the body.

TELENCEPHALON. The most anterior division of the brain is made up mainly of *olfactory centers,* the *basal ganglia,* and the *cerebral cortex.* In the lower vertebrates, the cerebrum developed in association with the olfactory bulbs, and there is a progressive increase in the relative size of the bulbs and associated cerebral olfactory centers through the infraprimate mammals. In the primates, however, the olfactory bulbs are relatively small, and the additional development of the cerebrum is unrelated to smell. The basal nuclei of lower vertebrates function as the highest motor integration mechanism, but in the mammals, the most complex motor functions are carried out by the cerebral cortex, particularly the motor cortex. The cerebral cortex is a grey mantle, or bark, of nerve-cell bodies that overlie the cerebrum. Its development is illustrated in Fig. 5-6. The oldest parts of the cortex (paleopallium and archipallium) are largely olfactory and visceral in function. The new cortex, or *neocortex,* appears in the reptiles as a receiving area for sensory fibers from lower regions of the brain. As it expands in size in the mammalian series, two things happen: (1) The paleocortex moves to a more ventral position and the archipallium, now the hippocampus, folds into the cerebral mass underneath the neocortex; (2) The neocortex expands so much that it begins to fold in on itself, developing the fissures, or sulci, and the bulges, or gyri, that characterize the convoluted brain. Using the major fissures as landmarks, we can divide the cortex into major lobes, as Fig. 5-7 shows for man.

Early in mammalian evolution, the neocortex is primarily a sensory receiving area (Fig. 5-8). Thus, the rabbit and the rat, whose cortices are convoluted very little, have fairly well-organized and somewhat segregated areas for vision, hearing, somatic sensation, and taste that occupy most of their cortical surfaces. The motor area, anterior in the cortex, is relatively small and not highly organized, and there are very few and small areas in the cortex that are neither sensory nor motor, but associational in function. In the carnivores (cat), the amount of associational cortex is increased, but the real increase in associational cortex occurs in the primates, especially in man (Fig. 5-9), where only relatively small strips of cortical tissue are devoted to sensory and motor function, and most of the cortex is given over to large association areas.

Despite their relatively small size, the sensory and motor areas of the human cortex become highly organized and represent, in great detail, the functional parts of the body and the receptor surfaces. For example, electrical stimulation of the human cortex reveals that simple, discrete movements in localized regions of the body can be evoked by stimulation of discrete points on the cortex. In fact, a map can be made of the motor area, showing the orderly representation of body parts, laid out in the pattern of a homunculus (Fig. 5-11). A similar map or sensory homunculus (Fig. 5-10) can be made of the somatic sensory area by stimulating receptors in the skin and recording the evoked potentials in the cortical area. As the figures show, the amount of cortex devoted to a given part of the body is related to its functional importance, particularly its sensitivity and the fineness of its motor control. Other sensory receiving areas of the cortex are similarly organized so that the receptor surface is represented spatially on the cortex. In fact, each sensory system is represented in the cortex in at least two closely related, but separated, areas, each organized to represent the receptor surface.

As we shall see later, destruction of these separate cortical sensory areas results in defects in sensory capacity, but in examining the mammalian series, we find that the sensory functions appear "corticalized" to different degrees. Thus, destruction of the visual area in monkey and man results in virtually total blindness; the rat and the cat, in contrast, while deficient in ability to see patterns after visual cortex damage, are

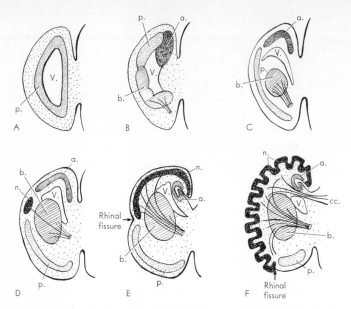

Fig. 5-6. Diagram showing the development of the cerebral cortex in the verte-brates. At first, there is a collection of cell bodies deep within the hemispheres (A and B). As the early reptilian stage is reached (C), the cell bodies appear on the surface as a mantle or true cortex. This is old cortex, divided into paleopal-lium ventrally and archipallium dorsally. In later reptilian stages, the neocortex appears as a small area between the two regions of old cortex (D). In early mammals, the neocortex enlarges (E), and in more advanced mammals (F), this enlargement of neocortex is so great that it not only occupies the whole dorsal and lateral surface of the cerebrum but also must fold in on itself to fit into the confines of the cranial vault. Note that the archipallium has folded into the internal mass of the cerebrum dorsally (E and F) and that the paleopallium is now a small ventral and medial part of the cortex in F. (a., archipallium; b., basal nuclei; cc., corpus callosum; n., neopallium; p., paleopallium; V., ventricle.) (Re-drawn from Romer.)

Fig. 5-7. Lateral view of the human cerebral cortex, showing the major division into lobes. (Redrawn from S. W. Ranson and S. L. Clark, The Anatomy of the Nervous System. Philadelphia: Saunders, 1959.)

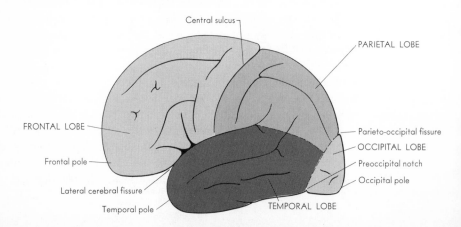

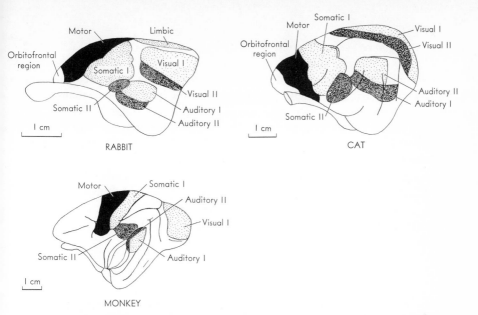

Fig. 5-8. Maps of the sensory and motor areas of the cerebral cortex of representative mammals. Note that in the mammals relatively less and less cortex is devoted to sensory and motor functions and more and more to associational functions (cf. Fig. 5-9). (Redrawn from J. E. Rose and C. N. Woolsey, "Organization of the Mammalian Thalamus and Its Relationships to the Cerebral Cortex," EEG Clin. Neurophysiol., **1**, 1949, 391.)

Fig. 5-9. Lateral view of the cortex of man, showing the relatively small areas devoted to sensory and motor function and the relatively large areas to associational function (cf. Fig. 5-8). (Redrawn from J. C. Brash, Cunningham's Manual of Practical Anatomy, **Vol. III.** London: Oxford University Press, 1948.)

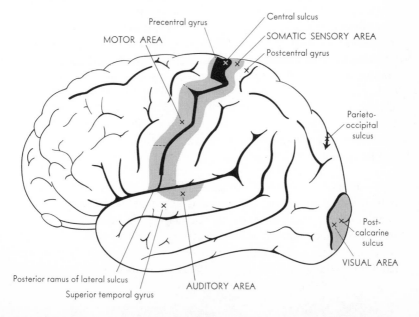

quite capable of telling light from dark, responding to movement, etc. Even more striking evidence for corticalization in the mammalian series is seen with destruction of the motor areas, for an animal like the rat shows essentially no obvious motor defects after such an operation, whereas the limbs of monkeys and men are badly paralyzed on the opposite side of the body following destruction of the motor area. Cats and dogs show some paralysis and poverty of movement, but show much more recovery of function than the primates. It takes very careful and somewhat elaborate testing to see the effects of destruction of associational cortex, and usually such defects show up only in man and monkeys, as we shall see later.

FUNCTIONAL ORGANIZATION
OF THE VERTEBRATE NERVOUS SYSTEM

Thus far in our effort to portray the major changes that have occurred in the evolutionary development of the vertebrate nervous system, we have revealed only the barest outline of its basic plan. The key to this plan lies, as it does in the invertebrate nervous system, in the concept of the reflex arc, with its sensory, motor, and associational neurons. Through the great ascending and descending columns of the spinal cord, this sensory-motor arc is extended into the brain, where, at various levels, additional sensory-motor integrations occur through even more complex networks of associational neurons. Let us look more closely at the organization of this system, taking the primate as our example.

On the sensory side, the great afferent systems are organized anatomically and physiologically in such a way that they reveal within the central nervous system a detailed representation of sensory qualities and spatial relationships established at the peripheral receptor surfaces. In representing sensory qualities, the afferent systems are said to be *modality-specific* in two respects. First, the different senses themselves are anatomically segregated into different parts of the nervous system representing vision, hearing, smell, taste, and the skin and muscle senses. Second, within a given sense, as we know from the study of both man and animals, there is a segregation of such sensory qualities as touch, warm, cold, deep pressure, and pain in the skin or the different pitches of sound from high to low. In addition, because spatial relationships established at the peripheral receptor are also preserved anatomically and physiologically within the central nervous system, they are said to be *somatotopically* organized, as the homunculus in Figs. 5-10 and 5-11 shows. Not only is this somatotopic arrangement apparent in the cortex, but, as one might expect, it is preserved to one degree or another at each level of the sensory relay systems below the cerebral cortex.

At the same time that each sensory system is kept highly segregated from the others and highly differentiated within itself, it also makes a

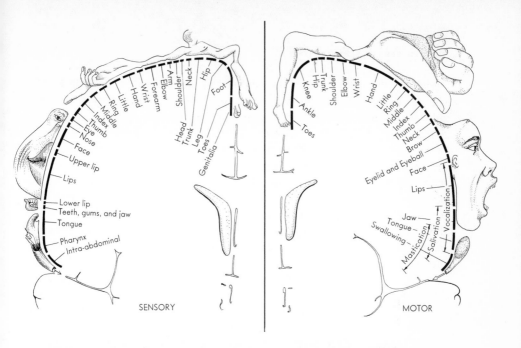

Fig. 5-10. (Left) Diagram of section cut through a human brain, showing the representation of body parts as measured by evoked potentials recorded from each point of the cortex upon stimulation of the skin at the parts of the body shown. (Redrawn from W. Penfield and T. Rasmussen, The Cerebral Cortex of Man. New York: Macmillan, 1952.)

Fig. 5-11. (Right) Diagram of a section cut through a human brain, showing the representation of parts of the body on the motor cortex as points eliciting movements, when electrically stimulated, of the parts of the body shown. (After Penfield and Rasmussen.)

fairly nonspecific contribution to a diffuse, sensory arousal system, located in the midline regions of the brain. Each ascending column, early in its course, gives off collateral nerve connections to the core of the brain; this is known as the *reticular system,* and does not seem to preserve receptor-surface locus or sensory modality. The reticular system is literally a felt-work of intermingling and interconnecting nerves that runs on up to the midline region of the thalamus, and from there to all parts of the cerebral cortex and, indeed, to many other parts of the brain as well. Its function seems to be generally to activate or arouse the brain upon receipt of sensory stimuli at the peripheral sense organs. Destruction of this reticular system results in coma or deep sleep, even though the main ascending columns are left intact. In this condition, an organism can transmit sensory information to its cerebral cortex along its ascending columns, but cannot be aroused to act upon it.

On the motor side, there are also two major systems. One is the long, discrete *pyramidal system* going from the motor cortex to the motor nerves of the spinal cord. This system, as we have described, is highly specific and localized, for electrical stimulation of the motor cortex results in discrete localized movements of limited parts of the body (Fig. 5-11). Also, damage to it results in a loss of refined and skilled movements of the hands and feet. The second motor system is the *extrapyramidal system* arising from different parts of the cortex and various subcortical motor centers as well, including the cerebellum. Its pathway is made up of short neurons that make connections at many levels of the brain before reaching the motor nerve cells of the spinal cord. In simple terms, the extrapyramidal system functions to maintain an organized background of posture and muscle tone against which the discrete, localized movements mediated by the pyramidal paths can occur.

Sensory and motor systems are not by any means wholly separated from each other, however. Motor influences from the brain reach down into the sensory systems at many levels and modulate the activity coming into the central nervous system. In some cases, motor neurons go directly to the receptors themselves (e.g., stretch receptors in muscles). In other cases, they send branches to connect with the sensory paths at some relay station within the brain. The sensory systems, on the other hand, are continually active in bringing back to the central nervous system information on the effects of motor activity by means of feedback loops, so that subsequent motor output may be modulated by the sensory effects of previous motor activity.

Associational systems serve to integrate the sensory activity coming into the nervous system over many different sensory nerves and to impose an organized pattern on the motor output, thus playing a most important role in the organization of behavior. Presumably, this activity of the associational system is determined by its given structure, the effects of past experience, motivation, and attention, as well as by the direct consequence of sensory input; further, in man, the associational systems are probably responsible for that intrinsic pattern of activity of the central nervous system known as thinking.

So far we have only discussed what has been called the somatic nervous system, which is concerned with perception, response of the skeletal muscles, and overt behavior. There is also the *autonomic nervous system,* which regulates visceral and emotional functions. This is a system interwoven with the somatic system at all levels. At the spinal level, it is represented by two sets of peripheral ganglia, the sympathetic and parasympathetic systems, both of which innervate the smooth muscles of the gut and blood vessels and many of the endocrine glands. In the brain, important autonomic functions are integrated in the medulla, the hypothalamus, and the older parts of the cortex known as the rhinencephalon.

SUMMARY

We can now summarize the major principles of action of the vertebrate nervous system.

1. It is a vast *correlation system* for receiving sensory information, integrating it, and associating it with appropriate patterns of motor responses.

2. Its *sensory systems* serve to carry faithfully reproduced information to the brain, and at the same time, through the reticular activating system, they serve to keep the brain active and the organism alert.

3. As we saw in the spinal cord, the nervous system acts according to a principle of *reciprocal pattern of excitation and inhibition* so that as one activity is started, another antagonistic activity is slowed or stopped.

4. Its *motor systems* serve to maintain a background of posture and tone against which discrete, phasic movements are executed.

5. The sensory and motor systems mutually modulate each other through motor control of sensory input and sensory feedback of the effects of motor activity, allowing the greatest degree of refinement of both sensitivity and movement.

6. Its *associational systems* serve to correlate the various sensory influences coming into the brain and to integrate them with past experience to impose an organized pattern of excitatory and inhibitory activity upon the execution of behavior over the motor pathways.

7. Its *autonomic system,* organized in a parallel sensory-motor plan, serves to control visceral and endocrine activities and emotional and motivated behavior.

8. Despite this artificial separation into systems, the *action of the nervous system is integrated* into an organized whole serving the behavioral adaptations of the organism.

9. There is in this organized whole a *hierarchical order of integrations,* with reduplications of functional mechanisms at various levels of the nervous system.

10. In keeping with the evolutionary process of *encephalization,* the more complex integrations are mediated by the more anterior and more recently evolved neural mechanisms.

Stereotyped
Behavior

CHAPTER SIX

Up till now, we have been mainly concerned with the basic biological machinery for behavior. We have discussed the evolution of the nervous system through the invertebrate and the vertebrate series, showing how the complexity of the nervous system has grown in phylogeny and pointing out how this has made possible the great increase in the refinement, variability, and complexity of behavior. We have also discussed the physiology of neurons and networks of neurons to give you some understanding of the "language" of the nervous system, the means by which the multitudinous parts of the nervous system communicate with one another, how they receive information from the external world, encode it, integrate it, store it, and translate it into behavioral action. All along, we have emphasized that it is out of these anatomical and physiological properties of nervous tissue that behavior, as we observe it in organisms, is possible.

Now we come to a consideration of behavior itself and how it serves the adaptive ends of the individual organism and the species. Here we shall analyze animal behavior into meaningful units and see in some detail how it is dependent on the functioning of the nervous system. In making such an analysis of behavior, we must recognize that there is, in the phylogenetic series, an enormous range of complexity of behavior, from the simple, brief, stereotyped act to the highly intricate and highly variable long sequence of acts.

At first, in phylogeny, behavior is largely a matter of a stimulus triggering a response or of a pattern of stimuli triggering a sequence of responses. At this point, behavior is *stereotyped* and the organism is to a large extent *stimulus-bound*. Since this kind of behavior is essentially the outcome of the inherited properties of the nervous system of the organism or species in question, we speak of it as *innate*. Later, behavior becomes more variable and, what is particularly important for us, more modifiable through experience. The adaptations of an individual organism may develop uniquely in its life history through the process of learning, and we speak of such behavior patterns as being *acquired*. In the simpler organisms, what is acquired may be fairly simple and still pretty much stimulus-bound. But as the complexity of the nervous system grows and we examine the existing species of mammals, especially the primates and man himself, still new properties of behavior emerge. Behavior is now not so stimulus-bound; much of it may originate within the organism on the basis of past experience; and much of it may be guided by complex symbolic processes such as language in man. Such intrinsic processes constitute *reasoning* in man, and we see the rudiments of it in animal behavior serving the adaptive ends of the organism.

In this and the remaining chapters, we shall take up these various modes of adaptive behavior. First, we shall consider the major stereotyped, innate modes of adaptation, the *taxes* (direct orientations of the organism in respect to stimuli), the *reflexes,* and the *instincts.* In the next two chapters, we shall take up *learning ability* and *problem solution,* or *reasoning,* which are the more variable, acquired modes of adaptation. As you will see, the importance of these particular modes of adaptation to an organism changes in phylogeny (Fig. 6-1). In man, the dominant modes of adaptation are reasoning and learning; there is very little in the way of instinct or even reflex that is not greatly modified by experience; taxes are essentially nonexistent. In a simple mammal like the rat, in contrast, reasoning is virtually nonexistent, but learning is well developed; instincts are clearly present and important, but they may be modified by experience; some taxes are present, but only very early in ontogenetic development. The insects, relatively speaking, are poorer learners, are dominated by largely unmodifiable instincts, and show taxes quite clearly. Below the level of worms, learning is not clearly recognizable and may not be a property of organisms; instinctive patterns are relatively simple and poorly developed, and organisms are dominated by taxes and reflexes.

Although it is speculative to attempt to portray trends in the major

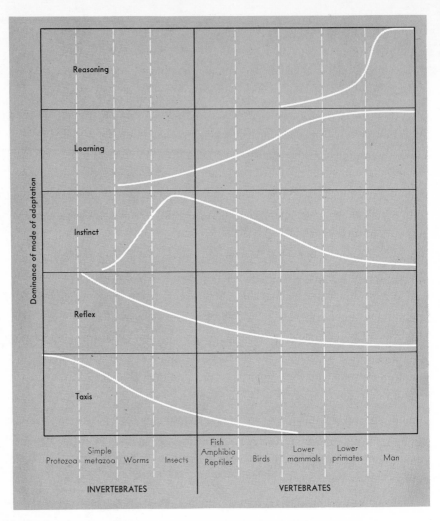

Fig. 6-1. Schematic portrayal of the changes that take place in the major modes of adaptive behavior in phylogeny. Reading from left to right, it shows the relative development of different modes of adaptation; reading up and down, it shows the relative pattern of modes of adaptation at different levels of the phylogenetic scale.

modes of adaptation in the course of evolution, especially in view of the great gaps in our knowledge, several important principles are apparent. (1) As complex modes of behavior become possible in phylogeny, they are at first added to the simpler modes, but eventually replace them. (2) At each new level of complexity, new behavioral properties emerge. (3) It is fallacious to try to account for the behavior of relatively simple organisms in terms of human capacities such as reasoning (Lloyd Morgan's Canon). (4) It is equally fallacious to try to account for the behavior of relatively complex organisms such as the lower primates and man primarily in terms of simple stimulus-bound relations, instincts, or blind trial-and-error learning. The primates have new modes of adaptation that overshadow the simpler ones, and we need a converse of Lloyd Morgan's Canon that will warn against underestimating the capacity of animals with complex nervous systems on the basis of principles discovered in the study of simpler organisms.

TAXES

Perhaps the simplest form of adaptive behavior is the orientation of an organism to some aspect of its environment. Not all orientations are taxes, however. In a very simple case, the orientation might be nothing more than a series of random movements coupled with occasional avoidance or approach movements in response to a specific stimulus. Thus *Paramecia* will congregate in a region of low CO_2. Whenever random movements bring them close to the bubble where CO_2 concentration is high, they swim backwards and turn and then swim forward again away from the bubble. This action is repeated over and over again with the result that most of the *Paramecia* of a group are situated at some distance from the bubble at any given instant (Fig. 6-2).

This kind of orientation does not qualify as a taxis, for its direction is not continuously guided by a specific stimulus. An example of a taxis would be orientation to maintain equal stimulation of two bilaterally symmetrical receptors or, by alternate left and right movements, equalization of stimulation at successive intervals over time. For example, an organism may orient toward a light source so that both eyes receive equal stimulation. If the source is moved laterally, the orientation will change, because one eye is now receiving more illumination than the other. If one eye is removed or painted over, the organism will move continuously in circles as though "trying" to equalize the light on the two eyes. Such an orientation, continuously and specifically guided by external stimuli, is called a *taxis*. Jacques Loeb, a pioneer in the study of this behavior, called this a tropism, but modern students reserve that term for the orientation of plants by growth (e.g., toward light, away from gravity).

Fig. 6-2. Diagram showing how random swimming movements of Paramecia **result in an orientation away from a CO₂ bubble. (Redrawn from Maier and Schneirla.)**

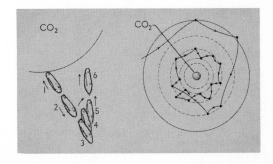

Although the essence of a taxis is the orientation, movement in respect to the stimulus may also be involved. In such cases, if the orientation and movement are toward the source of stimulation, we speak of a *positive taxis,* if away from it, a *negative taxis.* Taxes are also named in terms of the directing stimuli (e.g., *phototaxis, chemotaxis, geotaxis*).

The adaptive value of taxes can be seen in the case of the grayling butterfly (*Eumenis semele*), which flies toward the sun in its escape from predators; if one eye is blinded, however, its escape reaction will consist of flying in circles, which shows its dependence on bilateral optic stimulation. To illustrate that not all taxes depend on equal bilateral stimulation, this same butterfly will continue to pursue females in a straight path after unilateral blinding. The *light-compass reaction* of ants and bees is a taxis that can also occur with only one eye. In this case, moreover, the orientation is not simply toward or away from the stimulus source, but rather the organism orients and moves at some angle to the source of light. Thus, homing ants will change their direction in accordance with the change in position of the sun even when they are captured and kept in dark boxes (Fig. 6-3). Even if the sun is invisible, these insects are sensitive to the plane of polarization of light from the sky.

In the simplest case, such as that described by Loeb, a taxis may amount to a "forced" orientation or movement in which the organism's adaptation is a simple, automatic, innate pattern of response to sensory stimulation. In other cases, however, a taxis may be part of a more complex pattern of behavior, so that a natural orientation may depend on two or more taxes, or a given taxis may be imbedded in a complex in-

Fig. 6-3. Homing ants maintain orientation toward the nest by progressing at right angles to the sun. When captured and held at point X while sun moves 37° from position 1 to position 2, their path (shown in white) continues at right angles to the sun and then deviates from the path to the nest by 37°. (From Maier and Schneirla.)

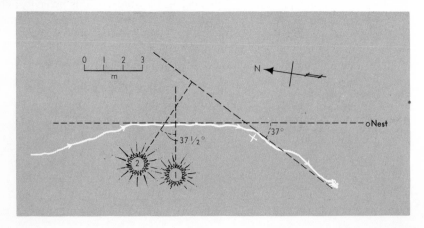

stinctive act. For example, the upright orientation of fish, ventral surface down, may depend on both photic and gravitational taxes. Thus, if light comes in from the side of a tank rather than from above, certain fish may orient at an angle upward or downward. If the effects of gravity are removed by destroying the labyrinth of the inner ear, the fish will orient perpendicularly with light from the side and even ventral side up if light comes from below (Fig. 6-4).

More complication is introduced when other processes or factors *interfere* with the basic orientation. Thus, the cockroach naturally avoids light, but it can temporarily reverse this natural orientation if it is always given an electric shock in the dark side of a compartment and never in the lighted side. In higher animals, a simple taxis may show up under very limited conditions, but is easily upset by the intrusion of other factors. Thus, the newborn rat, which has its eyes closed, will show a rather fixed orientation to gravity when it is placed on a wide inclined plane. Its natural tendency is to climb upward against gravity (negative geotaxis). The climb is not straight up the incline, however, but is at some angle to the left or to the right, and the size of the angle is determined by the steepness of the incline. The steeper the incline, the greater the angle of climb, approaching the straight upward path. But when the rat's eyes open, its behavior becomes more variable, and it responds visually to the edges of the inclined plane and the table top, so that it is very likely to deviate from a straight path upward and turn around and come down to the table surface. Although adult rats show some tendency to climb upward, they very quickly learn to escape from the inclined plane and will either jump off one side or turn and run down to the table.

Fig. 6-4. Reaction of Crenilabrus rostratus **to light coming from different directions (arrows). On the left is a normal fish; on the right, one that has had its response to gravity eliminated by the removal of the labyrinth of the ear. (Redrawn from Tinbergen.)**

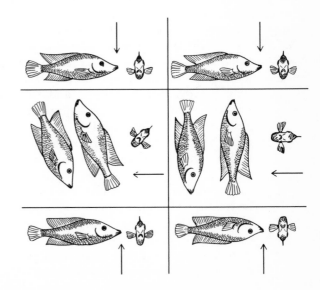

Thus, while it is possible to demonstrate many clear-cut instances of relatively fixed and stereotyped orientations to specific stimuli in the animal kingdom, not all taxes occur so simply in nature. Very early in the study of such behavior, H. S. Jennings pointed out that all animals, even protozoa, show great variability in their behavior and are not completely fixed in their orientation responses. The reason for this, of course, is that a living organism is responsive to more than one aspect of its environment and internal state at any given instant and may be making several different adaptations at once. The higher in the phylogenetic scale we go and the more modes of adaptation an animal has, the more variable is its behavior, and thus the less fixed and stereotyped its orientation. Nevertheless, it is clear that, under appropriate conditions, lower organisms will display to external stimuli certain *relatively* fixed and stereotyped reactions that we can designate with the term taxis. And often in observing complex patterns of behavior, we can identify component acts that are *relatively* fixed orientation responses imbedded in a more complex whole.

REFLEXES

Very similar to the taxes are the reflexes, for they are relatively stereotyped and fixed responses to stimuli that fit the definition of innate behavior in the sense that they are the outcome of inherited neural mechanisms. In fact, in many respects it is difficult to make a hard and fast distinction between taxes and reflexes. Generally speaking, taxes involve an orientation of the whole body that may involve a number of specific reflex responses. Reflexes, like the startle reflex or righting reflex, may involve all or most of the body, but, typically, they are responses of part of the body, like the flexion of a leg in response to painful stimuli or the constriction of a pupil to intense light. Quite clearly, such reflexes are adaptive and, as behavior goes, relatively invariable. Yet it doesn't take much observation of reflexes to see that there is some variation in them, especially in the higher vertebrates and in reflexes dependent on levels of the nervous system above the spinal cord.

In general, there are two classes of reflexes. The *tonic reflexes* are relatively slow, long-lasting adjustments that maintain muscular tone, posture, and equilibrium. The *phasic reflexes,* on the other hand, are rapid, short-lived adjustments such as that seen in the flexion response. Reflexes may be organized at various levels of the nervous system and may occur in varying degrees of complexity; usually those with greater complexity depend on the higher segments of the nervous system. In vertebrates, as we pointed out earlier, simple flexion and extension reflexes, including stepping, may be organized within a few segments of the spinal cord. But the coordinated alternation of flexion and extension that is locomotion is organized over many segments of the spinal cord and normally requires the influence of the midbrain. The same is true of the righting reflexes, which involve complex patterns of responses for keeping the head and body lined up and both of them upright in respect to gravity.

Many patterns of behavior are complex arrays of simple reflexes. At one time, it was believed that all complex behavior could be understood fully in these terms and that even learning and thought were nothing but complex combinations of innate and conditioned, or acquired, reflexes. Although it is theoretically possible to analyze almost any behavior into its component reflexes, this has rarely been done with any degree of success, and it has been quite clear that many kinds of behavior—instinctive patterns for one—involve something more than complex chaining of simple reflexes with invariable stimulus-response relationships.

Nevertheless, the reflex response is one of the major modes of adaptation in the animal kingdom. In the course of evolution, however, reflexes become less prominent features of behavior, for they become more variable and more and more subject to modifying influences of the higher neural mechanisms, and are overshadowed by other modes of adaptation.

INSTINCTIVE BEHAVIOR

By far the most complex and most fascinating of the innate behavior patterns are the instincts. Unfortunately, many misconceptions have surrounded the concept of instinct in the past, for very early in its history, the term instinct implied some mysterious, vitalistic force which impelled the organism to action and directed its course with the infallible "wisdom of nature." Today we know that no special energy is released in instinctive behavior beyond the energy from the metabolic mechanisms that lie behind all the cellular activity involved in behavior. We also know that in many cases instinctive behavior is not an infallibly accurate "fixed pattern" of response, for there is too much variability in the behavior of even simple organisms, and the behavior of the higher organisms is constantly being modified and shaped by individual experience and learning. Furthermore, while it is clear that instinctive behavior is adaptive and has direction, so is all other behavior, and it is a serious teleological error to ascribe special purpose either to animals or to nature.

One early attempt to solve these difficulties was the establishment of three criteria for instinctive behavior. To be an instinct, a behavior would have to be (1) unlearned, (2) characteristic of the species, and (3) adaptive. Applying these criteria proved very difficult, however. We have already pointed out that "adaptive value" is not a criterion distinguishing instincts from other behavior. The first two criteria are even more difficult, especially in the case of "higher" animals, for it is not easy to control individual life experiences to the point where we can be sure learning has not contributed to a pattern of behavior. For example, not all cats kill mice, although this behavior is said to be instintive, for it turns out that kittens often must see adult cats killing mice before they do so themselves and that kittens reared with mice rarely become mouse-killers. Similarly, the chaffinch, if reared in isolation from its kind, sings a much simpler song than chaffinches reared with adult birds (Fig. 6-5), and they may never be able to learn the full song of the species if they are kept isolated from their kind past one breeding season.

Because it is so difficult to assess the criteria of instincts, many ardent believers in the concept were able to apply it all too freely in the past to almost every kind of behavior in every animal, including man. Worse than that, they used instinct as an explanatory concept, never seeking to analyze or investigate its underlying mechanisms. Thus it was said, for example, that man fought because he had a fighting instinct and that was all there was to it.

Modern understanding of instinctive behavior came about through the abandonment of these misconceptions in favor of direct, experimental investigation of these complex behavior patterns. Today, two rather different scientific schools are converging in their experimental investigations. One is that of the European ethologists, who are zoologists and who investigate behavior under natural or seminatural conditions. In their approach, they have sought full knowledge of the behavioral repertoire of the species they study in order to see instinctive behavior in its proper context. Their interest has been chiefly in animals other than mammals, and they have focused mainly on parental and filial behavior, social behavior, and reproductive behavior. The second group is made up pri-

Fig. 6-5. Records of the patterns of sound frequencies in normal chaffinches (A and B) and those reared in isolation from adults of their species (C). The isolated birds have only an incomplete song, showing the role of experience in the development of instincts. (From Thorpe.)

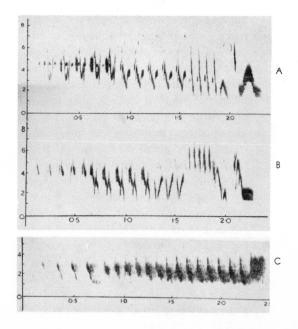

marily of American psychologists and physiologists, who are interested mainly in hunger, specific hunger, thirst, sexual behavior, temperature regulation, sleep, rage, and fear. These investigators have worked primarily on mammals, including primates and man himself. Typically, they have been interested in one limited aspect of behavior, observed under artificial laboratory conditions, but probed deeply for its neurophysiological mechanisms. Despite the differences in these approaches of these two scientific schools, it is remarkable how similar their findings and basic conceptions are.

We can begin with the viewpoint of the ethologists, for they have offered the most complete and most general conceptions. They make two important points that distinguish instinctive behavior from taxes and reflexes. First they stress how instinctive behavior so often depends on some special condition of the internal environment of the organism. For example, many aspects of reproductive behavior depend on the presence of the sex hormones, with the result that at one extreme there is no positive response to strong sexual stimulation in the absence of hormones, and at the other, when hormone concentration is high, only minimal stimulation is required to elicit a complete pattern of sexual behavior. In some cases, the internal state may be so strong as to lead almost directly to behavior without any measurable eliciting stimuli; this is the so-called *vacuum reaction*. The second point is that stimuli serve only to trigger instinctive behavior and are not always necessary to guide it through the entire pattern. The gray goose, for instance, will retrieve an egg that has rolled outside its nest by pushing it through its legs with the underside of its beak, and it may continue such diligent pushing movements to "completion" even if the egg has rolled away from it.

The ethologist conceives of instinctive behavior as a complex interaction of both internal and external influences, organized in a hierarchy of neural mechanisms with each level of the nervous system controlling specific instinctive acts. For example, the reproductive behavior of the male three-spined stickleback fish is made up of migratory, territorial, fighting, nesting, mating, and parental instinctive acts. Migration, believed to be organized at the highest neural level, is set off by increases in gonadal hormones produced by seasonal increases in daily light. Directed by temperature, the fishes move to warm, shallow fresh water, where they select a territory in response to the sight of green vegetation. Here they build a nest, defend the territory against intruding males, and attract females by the increased redness of their bellies and by executing a zig-zag dance, which leads the female to the nest. Finally, mating takes place, and when the eggs are fertilized, the males participate in their care by fanning them with movements of their fins.

In the ethologists' conception, each of the instinctive acts is held in check by a neural inhibiting mechanism that is released by the combined effects of hormones, external stimuli, and the excitatory influences of higher neural mechanisms. The external influences may be physical aspects of the environment such as light, water temperature, vegetation, nesting materials, etc. Or they may be some aspects of a living animal such as the swollen abdomen of the gravid female, the red belly of the intruding male, or his assumption of a threatening posture with nose downward. When the "releasing stimulus" is the behavior of another animal, we have an innate basis for social interactions and organization.

Careful experiments by the ethologists have shown how complex, and often how specific, these releasing stimuli may be. Thus, territorial defense in the stickleback may be elicited by a dummy fish with a red belly even if the dummy is not shaped like a stickleback. On the other hand, a faithful model of the stickleback fails to release fighting if it does not have the red belly (Fig. 6-6). Furthermore, it has been shown that more vigorous attack will be made if the stickleback is presented in the vertical position with nose downward rather than horizontally (Fig. 6-7).

Similar analyses have been made of other instinctive acts in other animals. The nestlings of the herring gull, for example, beg for food when presented with dummy gull heads. The strength of this response, however, depends on, among other things, the presence of a spot on the model's beak and its color (Fig. 6-8). In addition, the direction of the begging response is determined partly by the red spot and partly by the tip of the beak (Fig. 6-9). Release of the innate response, therefore, is determined by the whole pattern of stimulation provided. The importance of the configuration is seen even more dramatically in the escape reactions of young ducks and geese in response to the short neck of a bird of prey. When the dummy shown in Fig. 6-10 was sailed to the right, with the short neck leading, the escape reactions were elicited as though in response to a bird of prey. But when the dummy was sailed to the left, the long neck leading, presenting the pattern of a goose, there was no sign of any disturbance in the young birds.

Fig. 6-6. Fighting in the stickleback was elicited by the lower 4 models, which did not have the shape of the fish, but did have the red underside. The faithful model, lacking the red belly, did not elicit fighting. (Redrawn from Tinbergen.)

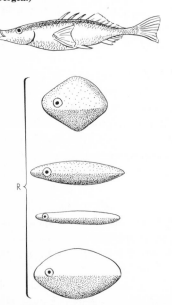

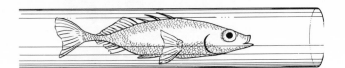

Fig. 6-7. When the three-spined stickleback is prevented from assuming its natural "threat-posture" (top diagram), it elicits far less fighting from other fish than the fish at right which is placed in the "threatening" posture. (Redrawn from Tinbergen.)

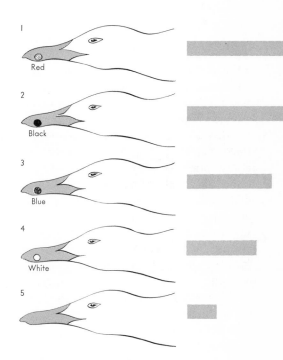

1 Red

2 Black

3 Blue

4 White

5

Fig. 6-8. Experiment with herring gull models shows that the strength of the begging response of the young (length of bar to right) depended on a spot on the beak, especially on a dark spot and on a red one. (Redrawn from Tinbergen.)

Fig. 6-9. The begging response of the young herring gull is directed about as often to the mouth (70 times) as it is to the red spot (74 times), shifted in this experiment from the beak to the head of the model.

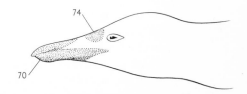

74

70

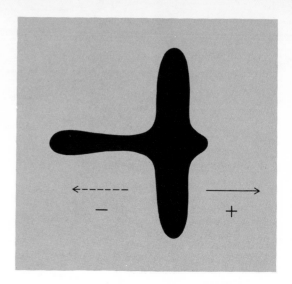

Fig. 6-10. When the model was sailed to the right, it elicited flight and escape in young ducks and geese; sailed to the left, it had no effect. (Redrawn from Tinbergen.)

MOTIVATED BEHAVIOR

The approach of American workers to problems of this sort is somewhat different. On the behavioral side, many American psychologists emphasize the *motivational* aspects of instinct and start with the conception that many patterns of instinctive behavior can be analyzed into *drive* directed toward a *goal,* the attainment of which results in reduction of the drive, or *satiation.* These terms may be illustrated by the case of a three-year-old boy with an abnormal craving for salt. From early life, he always preferred salty foods and would lick the salt off bacon and crackers rather than eat them. When he was 18 months old, he discovered the salt shaker and began eating salt by the spoonful. He learned very quickly to point to the cupboard and scream until he was given the salt shaker, and the first word he learned was "salt." It turned out that his craving for salt had kept him alive, for when he was taken to the hospital for observation and placed on a standard hospital diet with limited salt, he died within seven days. At autopsy, it was learned that he had tumors of the adrenal gland and thus lacked the hormones necessary to reabsorb salt at the kidneys. Only by constantly replacing salt lost in his urine did he maintain himself.

From this example, it can be seen that *drive* is a striving toward some goal (salt in our illustration). It is reflected in increased activity, a willingness to work or overcome some resistance to achieve the goal, and often by learning new instrumentalities of achieving the goal (screaming, pointing, saying the word "salt"). The *goal* itself may be an object that is acted upon or ingested as in the case of salt, or it may be the execution of a pattern of behavior as in mating. Or still more generally, it may be a change in the stimulation of the animal as in the escape from painful stimulation. New goals may be learned if they are instrumental in attaining the natural goal. Thus, a chimpanzee learns to work for poker chips that he later can redeem for food and water. *Satiation* is drive reduction. It is characterized by a reduction in activity and in willingness to work for the goal. *Motivated behavior,* then, is a drive that leads to goal-direct behavior and satiation. It may be measured by the intensity or rate of *consummatory behavior* such as in eating, drinking, and mating, or by the rate or intensity of work the animal will do to reach either the goal itself, some small fraction of it, or a learned goal such as the poker chips the chimpanzees associate with food.

On the neurophysiological side, motivated behavior, or instinctive behavior, has been investigated by tracing out the parts of the nervous system involved and the effects produced on them by external stimuli and changes in the internal environment. The focus of attention in work on mammals has been the *hypothalamus,* for it has been found to contain *excitatory mechanisms,* whose actions contribute to the arousal of motivated behavior, and *inhibitory mechanisms,* whose actions contribute to the reduction of motivated behavior. For example, in the case of feeding, investigators have discovered that destruction of the ventromedial regions of the hypothalamus on both sides results in a vast increase in eating, to the point where a rat or cat or monkey might double or triple its body weight. The ventromedial area qualifies, therefore, as a part of the inhibitory mechanism. Since bilateral destruction of the lateral hypothalamus will cause an animal to starve to death in the presence of its normal food, it can be thought of as an excitatory mechanism. Both these conceptions are borne out when electrodes are chronically implanted into these regions of the brain and just their tips are electrically activated while the animal is awake and active. In such a prepared animal, electrical stimulation of the lateral hypothalamus produces increased eating, and stimulation of the ventromedial hypothalamus causes a reduction in eating.

Similar, rather specific hypothalamic mechanisms have been found for thirst, sexual behavior, emotional behavior, sleep, and maternal behavior, and these findings have led to the notion that drive is based on the activity of an excitatory hypothalamic mechanism and that satiation is based on the activity of an inhibitory hypothalamic mechanism. It is also believed that the action of both these mechanisms is controlled by relevant sensory stimulation, changes in the internal environment, and influences from the cerebral cortex (Fig. 6-11). For example, it has been shown by recording the electrical activity of the hypothalamus that genital stimulation results in the rather specific activation of a small region of the hypothalamus whose destruction leads to the abolishment of sexual arousal. Experiments showing that appetite-depressant drugs selectively activate the inhibitory feeding mechanism in the ventromedial hypothalamus illustrate the influence of the internal environment. Even more dramatic are the cases in which small pipettes are implanted chronically into the region of the hypothalamus implicated in sexual behavior. Here injection of minute quantities of sex hormones produce prompt and vigorous mating behavior.

This type of experiment suggests there may be special chemical receptors in the hypothalamus that are selectively sensitive to the level of circulating sex hormones. Other experiments suggest that the hypothalamus may also contain temperature receptors and osmoreceptors. For example, injection of a few thousandths of a cubic centimeter of hypertonic saline into the hypothalamus of a goat will lead to prompt drinking of as much as seven liters of water, indicating that osmoreceptors may be involved in registering the cellular dehydration of thirst. It may be through mechanisms of this sort, then, that the internal environment plays its role in instinct and motivated behavior.

Fig. 6-11. Schematic diagram of the physiological factors controlling the excitatory and inhibitory hypothalamic mechanisms that govern motivated behavior.

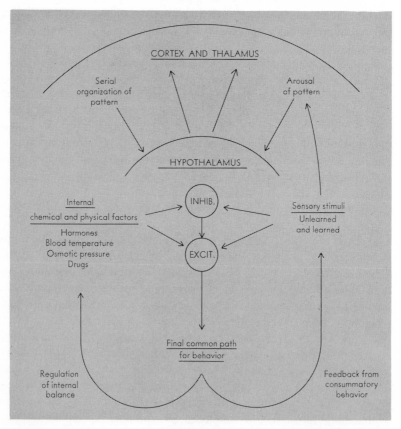

The role of the hypothalamus and other rhinencephalic structures in motivation can be seen on an even more general basis if a somewhat different kind of experiment is performed. In this case, an animal such as a rat, cat, or monkey is prepared with an electrode chronically implanted in the lateral hypothalamus, the septum, or the tegmentum. The animal is then placed in a situation where every time it pushes on a lever, a brief current is turned on, stimulating the point within the brain. Very quickly the animal comes to push the lever vigorously and rapidly, stimulating its own brain many times a minute for hours on end. That such self-stimulation behavior is strongly motivated is shown by the fact that the animals will push the lever many times for just a single stimulation, and, even more dramatically, they will walk across an electrified grid to push the lever even more readily than they will to eat when they are very hungry. Some places within the brain appear to be negative rather than positive, in that animals will stop pushing the lever if they are activated, or they will work hard to turn off such stimulation after the experimenter turns it on.

The role of the cerebral cortex is perhaps most clearly seen in emotional behavior. Here it has been found that destruction of the neocortex produces extreme placidity in cats, which suggests that the neocortex is essential for the arousal of aggressive behavior. On the other hand, destruction of parts of the old cortex results in unbridled ferocity. These cortical mechanisms, it is believed, have their influence through hypothalamic mechanisms known to be important in the arousal and control of aggressive behavior.

It is not surprising that, in the course of investigating the controlling neurophysiological mechanisms in many different species, we can trace out rather orderly changes in phylogeny. For example, in sexual behavior, the relative contributions of hormones, sensory stimuli, cortical influences, and learning undergo systematic changes in the mammalian series. If we compare rodents, carnivores, and primates, including man, we find a decreasing dependence on sex hormones and an increasing dependence on sensory stimuli, the cortex, and learning, to the point where the higher primates and man may not require hormones, but rather may be crucially dependent on learning. For example, whereas a rat reared in isolation will mate successfully in its first experience, a monkey isolated past puberty may be totally incapable of mating behavior.

In feeding behavior, similar changes can be traced over even a wider range of the animal kingdom. The blowfly responds with chemoreceptors to the chemical aspects of food and, through its central nervous system, either accepts or rejects foods. The stronger the stimulus, the stronger the reaction regardless of the actual food value of the chemical. Eating proceeds until sensory adaptation occurs or until an internal stimulus associated with the presence of food in the foregut is produced. If the nerves from the foregut are severed, there is no lasting cessation of eating. The blowfly, therefore, is quite stimulus-bound.

The rat is also highly responsive to the stimulus aspects of food and will eat nonnutritive sweet substances like saccharine. At the same time, however, it may regulate its intake according to the caloric content of food, and it is strongly affected by previous experience or learning. For example, a thiamine-deficient rat selects food containing thiamine. But if this food is first flavored with anise and the anise is then shifted to a food without thiamine, the deficient rat will forego the thiamine that will fulfill its need and select the anise-flavored, nonthiamine food in accordance with its habit.

Even more dramatic is the case of adrenalectomized rats. These animals, like the boy with the adrenal tumors, typically make up for the salt they lose in the urine by drinking large quantities of strong salt solutions, and thus manage to survive. If they have had the opportunity to drink sugar water before being operated on, however, they continue to prefer it to salt solution and die of salt deficiency. Controls that never had sugar solutions before operation and thus never developed a habit of sugar preference show a preference for salt over sugar and survive adrenalectomy. Habit, therefore, can be strong enough to be fatal. It plays an even greater role in man than it does in animals, for the regulation of our food intake and food preferences and aversions are as much a matter of early life experiences, personality, dietary laws, and social culture as they are of nutritional requirements.

SUMMARY

In this chapter, we have discussed a variety of stereotyped behavior that serves in the adaptation of an organism, from simple taxes and reflexes through complex instincts. Taxes are innate responses of the whole organism in orientation toward or away from stimuli; they are the resultant of inherited properties of the organism's receptors and central neural connections and are prominent in the adjustments of the lower invertebrates to their environment. Reflexes are also innate sensory-motor responses, usually of a part of the body. These are seen in all metazoa and are likewise determined by receptor properties and central neural connections. But reflexes may complexly interrelate with one another, sometimes in elaborate patterns of response, and with the development of learning capacity, they may readily be modified, as we shall see in the next chapter.

Instincts are the most complex of the stereotyped behaviors. In the lower organisms, they are innate responses that are elicited by the combined influences of the internal environment and sensory stimulation. In a sense, the internal environment "primes" the response mechanism, and the sensory stimulation triggers it, with the result that a complex neural mechanism may be set into action, yielding a complex sequence of behavior. In the higher organisms, this innate mechanism may be greatly modified by learning, and indeed overshadowed by learning, to the point where it is difficult to recognize instincts as such. By this time in phylogeny, the motivational aspects of instinctive behavior emerge clearly, and it is quite meaningful to talk about "drives," "goal-directed behavior," and "satiation." In mammals, it is believed that the arousal of drive is the result of the activation of an excitatory neural mechanism in the hypothalamus and that the reduction of drive, or satiation, is the result of the activation of an inhibitory hypothalamic mechanism. It is through these basic mechanisms that the combined effects of the internal environment, sensory stimuli, cortical influences, and learning regulate motivated behavior.

Learning

CHAPTER SEVEN

Of all the behavioral characteristics of living organisms, perhaps none is as striking as the ability to learn. This is the process through which life experiences leave their mark on an individual and the one that permits an animal to develop new adaptations in the light of past experiences, and sometimes to develop what turn out to be maladaptations. There are many kinds of learning, ranging from the simplest modifications of innate behavior to the most complex, symbolic transactions seen in the reasoning of man. All, however, are characterized by an enduring change in the behavior of the organism, perhaps a permanent change. From a biological point of view, the change in behavior must be a change in the functioning of the nervous system, and, if it is a permanent change, perhaps it is also a change in the structure of the nervous system.

By insisting that the change in learning must be a lasting one, we automatically rule out the transient changes resulting from sensory adaptation, fatigue, and fluctuations in motivation. Changes due to growth and maturation are harder to distinguish, for they are also permanent ones, and it often takes careful experimental procedures to separate the effects of maturation from the effects of learning. One obvious way is to try to hold experience constant over the period of time maturation can be expected to occur. This has been done successfully in the case of swimming behavior in salamanders, where one group of animals was anesthetized just before swimming movements developed and not released from anesthesia until after a control group of animals had developed to the point where they were swimming normally. Since the experimental salamanders swam essentially normally as soon as they recovered from the effects of anesthesia, it is obvious that this change in behavior was mainly a matter of maturation rather than the result of experience or learning.

The experiment, of course, is much harder to do in the higher animals, but an approximation of it has been successfully achieved in man. In this case, identical twins were used. One twin was allowed extensive experience in climbing stairs and the other was restricted to flat surfaces. This time, maturation was held relatively constant and experience allowed to vary. Again, experience turned out to be a relatively insignificant factor, for the second twin was as good as the first when finally given the opportunity to climb stairs.

Despite the value of these experiments, the most direct and obvious way to be sure that learning is taking place is to associate the change in behavior with some deliberate training procedure. This is the method employed by students of learning who are interested in investigating the phenomenon itself and in specifying the natural laws governing the process, and this is the method, in its various forms, that we shall mostly discuss in this chapter. Our purposes will be: first, to describe various kinds of learning from simple to complex; second, to try to arrive at general laws of learning; third, to see how the capacity to learn varies in phylogeny; and fourth, to summarize what we know of the neurophysiological basis of learning.

IMPRINTING

We can begin our discussion with a highly specialized and limited form of learning called *imprinting*. This is a phenomenon seen most clearly in birds during the very early period of their lives following hatching. In a young bird it consists simply of learning to follow the first large, moving object it sees and hears in a manner reminiscent of the natural tendency of the bird to follow its mother. For example, if a duckling is hatched in the presence of a large green box containing a ticking alarm clock, it will follow the movement of the box along a trolley wire. After some exposure to the box, the duckling will follow it rather than its own mother or other birds. Quite clearly this is a case of learning, for the bird can be imprinted in this manner on almost any suitable object, animal, or person. But it must depend on some special condition of the nervous system prevailing only early in development, for if the bird is not imprinted soon after hatching, it may never imprint at all.

HABITUATION

Perhaps the simplest kind of learning seen throughout life is *habituation*. In this type, upon repeated exposure to a stimulus, an animal gradually decreases its natural response until it may disappear entirely. Thus, an animal will orient toward a moderate sound, but with each successive exposure, it orients less and less until it orients no longer. That this change is not merely fatigue or sensory adaptation is clear, for the decrement in response grows with daily exposures to the stimulus and will last over long periods of time without stimulation. In a sense, habituation represents the dropping out of responses that are of no "significance" in the life of the animal. Most of the rest of learning is concerned with the strengthening of responses that are of "significance" so that they may be evoked more readily and with increased frequency or probability.

CLASSICAL CONDITIONING

One very simple form of learning of the latter type is *classical conditioning,* so called because it was discovered by Pavlov, the father of conditioning. In his classical experiment, Pavlov lightly restrained a dog in a harness and repeatedly blew meat powder into its mouth and recorded accurately the amount it salivated. Then he associated the sound of a bell with the meat powder and repeated this procedure many, many times at successive intervals. The bell, of course, did not at first elicit salivation, but after repeated pairings with meat, it came to do so. In describing this experiment, Pavlov called the salivation to the bell a *conditioned reflex* (CR), the bell a *conditioned stimulus* (CS), the salivation to the meat an *unconditioned reflex* (UCR), and the meat itself an *unconditioned stimulus* (UCS). The same experiment has been repeated many times on different animals and with many different stimuli and responses. For example, the UCR may be a flexion of a leg in response to electric shock to the foot (UCS), and if this reflex is paired with the sound of a metronome (CS), that signal will eventually cause a leg flexion (CR) (Fig. 7-1). Typically, the CR is similar to the UCR, but it is never completely identical to it. Thus, the best way to describe classical conditioning is as *a process in which a previously neutral stimulus (CS = bell) is enabled to elicit a response (CR = salivation) that it never elicited before training.*

In his experiments, Pavlov found that the time relation between the CS and the UCS was critical. If the UCS preceded the CS, there was very little, if any, conditioning, and if the CS preceded the UCS by more than about a second, conditioning became more and more difficult to establish (Fig. 7-2). Furthermore, he found that as he repeatedly paired the CS and

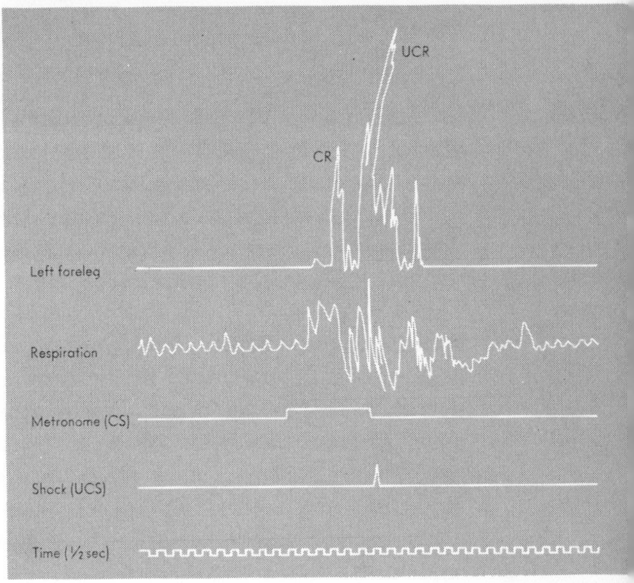

Fig. 7-1. Graphic record of a conditioned leg flexion and a conditioned respiratory response in the sheep, following the pairing of the sound of a metronome with shock to the foot for many trials. Note that the unconditioned flexion response is larger than the conditioned response. (Redrawn from E. R. Hilgard and D. G. Marquis, Conditioning and Learning. **New York: Appleton-Century, 1940.**)

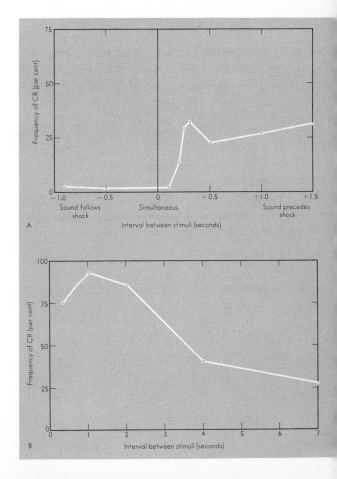

Fig. 7-2. Two separate experiments illustrate the importance of temporal relations between the CS and UCS in conditioning: (A) the difficulty of establishing "backward conditioning" where the UCS precedes the CS in human eyelid conditioning, and (B) the reduction in the strength of conditioning as the CS-UCS interval increases in conditioned respiratory response in the rat. (Redrawn from Hilgard and Marquis.)

UCS the strength of the CR grew steadily throughout the course of *acquisition* of the CR (Fig. 7-3). On the other hand, if he presented the CS alone repeatedly, the strength of the CR decreased steadily in what he called the *extinction* of a conditioned response. He concluded, therefore, that there was something about the presentation of the UCS that was essential for the strengthening and maintenance of the conditioned response. This "something" he called *reinforcement*. Some workers believe that reinforcement is a reward involving the reduction of a drive, because the dog received meat powder in one case and escaped from painful stimulation of the foot in the other. We shall shortly see cases where reinforcement appears quite clearly to be a drive reduction or reward. In classical conditioning, however, Pavlov believed that the reinforcement was nothing more than some effect in the nervous system produced by eliciting the unconditioned response during presentation of an ongoing conditioned stimulus.

Extinction, Pavlov believed, is a new learning that results in an inhibition of, or interference with, the CR. The reasons for this belief are as follows. If, early in training, a distracting stimulus (sudden noise) occurs as the CS is presented, there will be a great reduction in the CR; this is called *external inhibition*. If the same distracting stimulus occurs early in extinction, there is an increase in the strength of the CR, called *disinhibition*, for it is presumably the result of removing the inhibiting or interfering effects of new learning by external inhibition of that new learning.

Fig. 7-3. The acquisition and extinction of a conditioned leg flexion response in a cat where a tactile CS was used, showing the increasing strength of the CR as a function of the number of trials over which reinforcement is given (acquisition) and the decreasing strength of the CR as a function of the number of trials without shock reinforcement (extinction).

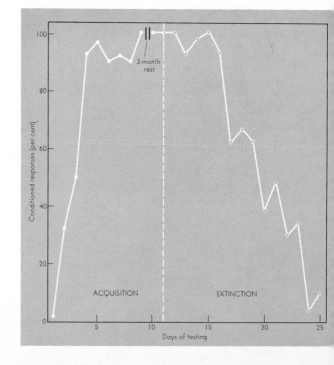

Two other concepts of Pavlov's will round out our summary of classical conditioning. One is the concept of *generalization,* which derives from the fact that an animal conditioned to one stimulus—say a 1000-cycles-per-second (CPS) tone—will also be conditioned to some degree to other similar stimuli—say a 500- or a 1500-CPS tone. Actually, there is a gradient of generalization in the sense that the farther a stimulus is away from the original CS along some continuum, the weaker is its capacity to elicit a CR. The second concept is *discrimination,* which is the result of reinforcing the CS (1000-CPS tone) and extinguishing a similar stimulus (say 1500-CPS tone) to the point where the animal always responds to the 1000-CPS tone and never to the 1500-CPS tone. As Pavlov pointed out, these conditioning and discrimination techniques not only afford a way to study animal learning, but also provide the opportunity for objective study of sensory capacities. For example, if we wish to learn something about the sensitivity of a dog's hearing, we can use the discrimination-training method described above to tell us the smallest difference in frequency the animal can distinguish, a value which turns out to be as low as a two-cycle-per-second difference.

From these facts about classical conditioning, we can derive a number of general laws that are remarkably similar to the laws of association described by the English association philosophers and later students of human verbal learning. The first is the *law of contiguity,* which says that items to be associated must occur together in time and place. We have seen how conditioning grows less and less effective as the interval between CS and UCS-UCR is lengthened. The second is the *law of repetition,* and Pavlov's studies showed that the strength of a CR grows progressively as more and more pairings of CS and UCS are made. The third law is the *law of reinforcement,* which describes a process that is essential to the strengthening of a CR. In certain forms, this law may be identical with the *law of effect,* which says that reward strengthens associations and punishment weakens them, presumably by training interfering escape and avoidance responses. The fourth law might be called the *law of interference;* it covers the case of extinction, or forgetting, and states that a conditioned response may be weakened and indeed inhibited by new learning that interferes with it.

The case for an interference concept of extinction and forgetting is perhaps best argued on the basis of data on human verbal learning. Here the degree of forgetting is a function of the activity intervening between learning and test of memory. If the intervening activity involves learning of verbal material similar to that originally learned, interference is marked and forgetting will be the greatest. If the intervening activity is totally different from the material originally learned, then forgetting is slight. And most interesting of all, if a person goes to sleep after the original learning, there is the least forgetting in the test of memory.

If extinction and forgetting are the result of interference, then it may be that *learning is permanent* and is merely covered over or inhibited by new learning. Pavlov's discovery of disinhibition supports this notion, and so do the studies where learning survives so completely through a period of sleep. But even more convincing are experiments where pigeons were trained in a simple response and then removed from the learning situation so that there could be no possibility for new learning that would interfere, that is, no opportunity for extinction. After ten years, these pigeons retained their original learning about as well as after a few days.

The case of classical conditioning is a case of passive learning where the experimenter elicits the desired response by reflex and presents the CS on schedule. The animal can do very little about it. He has to salivate or flex his leg each time the CS is paired with the UCS and his response produces no change in this situation. The experimenter has virtually complete stimulus-control over the animal and almost completely controls his responses, and the learning is distilled down to the point where the animal simply learns to make a new response to the stimulus.

INSTRUMENTAL CONDITIONING

Many kinds of learning are more complicated than that seen in classical conditioning, for animals have some control over the stimuli they receive and often the responses they use, and their behavior has some effect on their situation. For example, an animal may learn to depress a lever or a switch in order to get food delivered to him or to escape from electric shock or simply to escape confinement (Fig. 7-4). In these cases, the animal's behavior is instrumental in bringing about some significant change in his environment. Thus, we call simple instances of this kind of learning *instrumental conditioning*. Although the animal is now in a quite different training situation, the same phenomena of acquisition and extinction, and the same laws of contiguity, repetition, reinforcement, and interference apply. In instrumental conditioning, the animal starts out naively emitting a variety of responses that are in his natural repertoire. The trainer may

Fig. 7-4. A cat operating a bar to unlock a door and escape. (From Munn.)

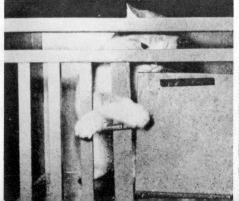

then select one response to reinforce: depressing a lever, standing on its hind legs, turning right rather than left at the end of an alley, etc. Because of the reinforcement, this response is emitted with greater frequency, and other responses drop out, or habituate.

Where the reinforcement involves the satiation of a drive, as in the case of the hungry animal depressing a lever or turning right to receive food, we call the training *reward training*. Where the reinforcement involves the escape from some noxious situation, such as electric shock, bright lights, or cold water, it is *escape training*. And where the reinforcement involves the possibility of avoiding noxious stimulation altogether, we call it *avoidance training*. For example, an animal receives a shock five seconds after a tone begins. At first, he can only escape the electric shock after it comes on by depressing a lever or leaping over a hurdle into a "safe" compartment, but later he may make the response within the five-second period between the onset of the tone and the onset of the shock and thus avoid the shock entirely. According to Pavlovian principles, one would expect the CR in this experiment to start extinguishing once the animal begins avoiding the shock (UCS) consistently, but extinction proves very difficult and the animal may continue responding for many, many trials without receiving shock. Apparently, the reinforcement in this situation is more than the shock itself. It has been suggested that this may be a special case of emotional reinforcement involving a "fear" of the shock that is reduced each time the animal makes the avoidance response. But this answer is by no means certain.

TRIAL-AND-ERROR LEARNING

Instrumental conditioning can be made complicated by simply increasing the complexity of either the stimulus situation or the response possibilities. This can be done by giving an animal a choice of stimuli to respond to, one with one response and the other with another response. For example, the animal may be confronted with two doors, one light and one dark. Food is available behind the light door; the dark door is locked, and the animal must learn to approach or jump to the light door whether it appears to the right or the left (Fig. 7-5). The animal here is required to make a discrimination of brightness, but the same test could be run using two different colors, a triangle and a circle, a loud and soft tone, etc. In this type of situation, the animal is more obviously involved in a process of *trial-and-error learning* in which correct responses are encouraged by reward and incorrect responses discouraged by withholding reward or, in some cases, by administering punishment.

Still more complicated is the multiple-choice maze in which the animal may be required to make a string of discriminations in order to thread its way through the maze to the food at the end (Fig. 7-6). In a typical maze, there may be several sensory cues at each choice-point that the animal

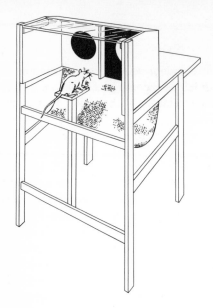

Fig. 7-5. A rat faced with a black-white discrimination in the Lashley jumping stand. If the black circle is correct, its door is open and food will be found behind it regardless of whether it is on the left or on the right. The other door with the white circle is always locked. (From Munn.)

could use as a basis for discrimination. Different animals may use different cues at the same choice-point; we can tell whether one rat uses a visual cue and another rat an auditory cue at a particular choice-point, because putting out the light causes only the first rat to make an error and eliminating auditory cues will affect only the second rat. The maze, then, is under multiple sensory control, and an animal may be left free to use any one of a number of alternative cues at each choice-point.

We have gone now from the simplest stimulus-response training of classical conditioning through more and more complicated instances of instrumental conditioning in which the sensory stimuli involved become more numerous and more complex and in which the animal is given a greater and greater measure of choice in the stimuli it uses. In general, as we go from the simple to

Fig. 7-6. Three mazes of graded difficulty used by Lashley to study the effects of brain lesions on learning in the rat. S is the start box and F the food box.

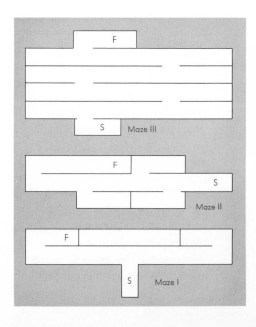

the complex learning tasks, learning becomes more difficult and more easily disrupted by brain injury. With these points in mind, it will be interesting to compare the learning ability of different animals that represent different levels of the phylogenetic scale and thus different levels of development of the nervous system.

PHYLOGENY OF LEARNING

The first question we may ask in comparing the learning ability of different animals is where on the phylogenetic scale the capacity to learn emerges. Is it a basic property of all animals? Or does it depend on development of the nervous system? If so, what properties of the system are required?

As we pointed out earlier in our discussion of protozoa (p. 7) and echinoderms (pp. 25 - 26), the experiments attempting to demonstrate learning in these organisms are not at all convincing. In each case, it turns out that the various instances of "modified" behavior, claimed to be learning, can be explained in terms of basic chemical and physical changes, independent of the training procedures. As it stands now, the burden of proof is on those who wish to claim that learning is possible in these organisms.

On the other hand, it is equally obvious that we cannot conclude that no learning is possible in protozoa and these simple metazoa. It is clear that it is difficult to carry out training procedures in these simple organisms without producing artifacts through injury or direct physical and chemical changes. Perhaps as we learn more about these organisms, we can design better learning experiments, but until then, we can make no claim for their ability to learn.

The first unequivocal evidence for learning is found at the level of the worms, where a bilaterally symmetrical, synaptic nervous system is already developed. Here we see clear instances of habituation and associative learning. In one experiment, earthworms were trained to go to one arm of a T-maze leading to a dark, moist chamber and to avoid the other arm, which led to electric shock and irritating salt solution (Fig. 7-7). In this simple learning of a position habit, it required about 200 trials on the average to reach a criterion of 90 per cent correct responses. Interestingly enough, the worms were able to retain what they had learned after removal of the first 5 body segments containing the cephalic ganglion; untrained worms could learn with the head ganglion removed. Apparently, the neural changes involved in learning can occur in the ganglia of the lower body segments.

Similar evidence has been offered in the case of the flatworm, the planarian. In this case, a classical conditioning technique was used. When the worms were gliding along in a trough of water, a light was turned on, followed two seconds later by an electric shock that caused the worms to contract longitudinally. After 150 trials, the worms contracted to the light alone over 90 per cent of the time. Following this, the worms were cut in half and allowed four weeks for regeneration. Both the regenerated head

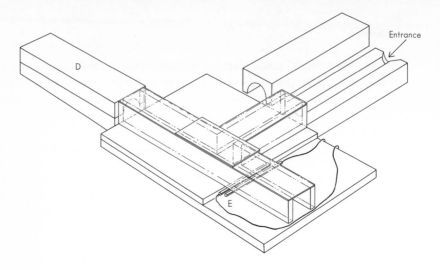

Fig. 7-7. A T-maze used by Yerkes for training earthworms to turn to the right to enter a dark, moist chamber (D) and to avoid electric shock at E on the left. (From Maier and Schneirla.)

and tail sections showed a high degree of retention of what had been learned earlier. Even after these regenerated worms were cut and a second period of regeneration occurred, there was retention of the conditional response. Apparently, in this case, too, learning is not confined to the anterior portion of the nervous system, but has an effect throughout its extent.

A word of caution is necessary here. Even though these experiments have presented clear findings and have been independently confirmed, some investigators have had difficulty reproducing them. For example, one attempt to condition the flatworm failed because the worms contracted to the light even before training. Possibly the light used was too intense or perhaps the worms were not in optimal condition at the time of the experiment. Even more disconcerting, some experiments suggest that flatworms become "sensitized" by the electric shocks so that they respond to the light alone even when the light and shock have never been presented together in training. All these difficulties are multiplied by the fact that in these classical conditioning procedures, the worm's responses are subjectively recorded, and the responses are not always clear enough to provide a basis for good observation. The use of instrumental learning procedures, such as the T-maze with earthworms, would eliminate the problems of recording responses objectively and avoiding sensitization. Attempts in this direction have thus far not been eminently successful.

We still have much to learn about these simple invertebrates, and until we know more, experiments of the sort described here will be fraught with difficulties and beset by inconsistencies. Nevertheless, the evidence at hand, especially on earthworms, makes it clear that we can conclude with some confidence that associative learning can occur at the level of the worms.

As we pointed out earlier (p. 40) clear evidence of learning has been offered in the case of the octopus with its well-developed eye and rather elaborate brain, but little can be said with confidence about learning in other molluscs.

Coming to the arthropods, we find much evidence for good learning. Bees can readily learn to fly to dishes placed on blue paper, for example, and avoid other dishes on gray paper if only the blue paper has been associated with sugar water. And they go consistently to the blue paper regardless of its relative position, even when all dishes are empty. Cockroaches and ants can learn simple mazes quite rapidly as experiments have shown. In the case of the ants, which are much better learners than cockroaches, the maze was interposed between the nest and the food, and learning was accomplished typically within 35 trials (Fig. 4-18). Apparently, the learning in this case was not highly general, for when the ants had to run from the food to the nest, they had to learn the true path all over again.

It is obvious by now that there has been relatively little experimental investigation of learning in the invertebrates, especially of the lower forms. We are still beset by our lack of knowledge of these simpler organisms, so that on the one hand it is difficult to test them under optimal conditions and, on the other, difficult to avoid experimental artifacts, or errors in interpretation. So far, positive evidence for learning is forthcoming only when we reach the level of the worms, which possess a bilaterally symmetrical, synaptic nervous system. Even more consistent and more complex learning is possible in the cephalopods and arthropods, with their large concentrated ganglionic masses, especially at the anterior pole of the central nervous system. Compared to the vertebrates, however, the higher invertebrates have relatively poor developed learning capacity. They are quite stimulus-bound, and their behavior in general is still dominated by the stereotyped patterns dictated by innate taxes, reflexes, and instincts.

We have already described many instances of vertebrate learning, so our treatment here may be brief and in rather general terms. Most of our knowledge is based on mammals, less on fish and birds, and the least on reptiles and amphibia, which have been very little studied. Fish have been successfully trained in a variety of discriminations involving simultaneous choice between two different objects. They have mastered mazes and detour problems much more rapidly and more consistently than invertebrates, with the possible exception of ants. Similar data have been obtained in a few studies on frogs and turtles. Modifiability and the ability to profit from experience, therefore, are clear characteristics of these animals. But by and large, their learning consists in trial-and-error learning of relatively simple stimulus-response relationships.

Birds show considerably more facility in learning than do the lower vertebrates, not only in the rapidity and consistency of learning, but also in the complexity of problems they are able to solve. In mammals, still further improvements are obvious as we compare simple mammals like the rat and the subhuman primates. By this phylogenetic stage, new behavioral capacities emerge that increasingly free the animals from simple stimulus-response, trial-and-error learning. Many items from past learning experiences are retained and utilized in new learning tests. The higher mammals are not as stimulus-bound and as slavishly restricted by habits as are the lower vertebrates. In fact, they bring to the solution of complex problems, as we shall see in the next chapter, rudimentary capacities for reasoning and symbolic behavior that put much of their learning on a rather different basis from that of the simpler organisms. Man, of course, is enormously liberated from the need to approach each problem in a simple trial-and-error manner. His symbolic capacity in the form of language allows him to call on accumulated past experiences rapidly and extensively and to profit from symbolic communications from others in the learning he undertakes.

Obviously, the comparison of learning ability among different species is a difficult task. At the same time that learning ability is improving in phylogeny, improvements in sensory capacity and manipulative ability are giving higher animals additional advantages, and, eventually, the capacities to solve problems by some form of rudimentary reasoning emerge as additional advantages of the higher animals.

NEURAL MECHANISMS OF LEARNING

If we were to attribute the improvement of learning ability to one thing in the phylogenetic series, it would be the evolution of the central nervous system. It is an article of faith that learning represents some change in the central nervous system, and that memory is the preservation of that change. From this starting point, many investigators have sought an answer to two major questions: (1) Where does learning take place in the nervous system, and (2) what is the nature of the change? We shall take up each of these questions separately although it is obvious that they are interrelated.

The question of the *locus of learning* has been approached mainly by the technique of experimentally destroying parts of the nervous system. Most investigators have dealt with the cerebral cortex, since the earliest theories held that it was in this newly evolved part of the brain that mammalian learning occurs. Pavlov believed that the cortex is essential for conditioning, but studies have shown that simple conditioning is possible in the dog after its cortex has been removed. Such a decorticate dog often gives emotional and generalized responses and is greatly deficient in sensory capacity, but it can be successfully trained in the classical conditioning technique using shock as the UCS.

Since total decortication grossly impairs an animal, many investigations of the cortex have involved the destruction of selected parts of the cortex. Thus, in his experiments on rats, K. S. Lashley removed just the visual area in the back of the cortex and tested the animals for visual learning and retention. He used a simultaneous discrimination situation in the jumping stand (Fig. 7-5) where the animal had to choose the correct one of two doors containing visual stimuli. When he used black and white doors, rats without the visual cortex could learn the discrimination almost normally. If they had learned to discriminate black from white before the lesion of the visual cortex, however, they lost the habit postoperatively and had to learn it all over again. When pattern discrimination was used involving a choice between a triangle and a circle, it turned out that the operated animals could never learn. Apparently in this case, they lost the capacity for form or detail vision, whereas in the brightness discrimination, capacity was unimpaired and only memory was affected.

Actually, however, further studies suggest that even in the brightness discrimination case, it was not memory that was affected, but rather it was a loss of sensory capacity needed to respond to the spatially separated black and white doors. To test this argument, dogs were confronted with a single, large, illuminated panel, shaped like a bowl so as to fill the entire visual field. Then they were conditioned to flex a leg every time the brightness of the field was changed. Here was a brightness discrimination not involving either spatial discrimination or the capacity to discriminate doors, and removal of the visual cortex had no effect on the animal's ability to retain it. So perhaps it was not a defect of memory that Lashley's brain lesions had caused.

Memory and learning ability also proved elusive in Lashley's maze experiments (Fig. 7-6). Here he found that rats were affected in their ability to learn mazes, or retain them, in proportion to the size of the cortical lesions he made in their brains. In other words, Lashley concluded that the cortex operates on a *mass-action principle* in learning and memory so that the larger the lesion, the poorer the ability. He also found that it did not matter where the lesion was in the cortex; a lesion of a given size had a given effect whether it was in the visual area in the back of the brain or the somatic sensory and motor areas in the front of the brain. From this finding, Lashley formulated his *principle of equipotentiality,* according to which all parts of the cortex are equal in their contribution to learning and memory. Again, it seems that these experiments may be as much a matter of sensory deficit following cortical lesions as they are the result of defects in learning and memory capacities.

Maze learning in a rat, we know, is a matter of learning to use many different sensory cues throughout the maze (vision, sound, touch, proprioception, smell). The more these cues are experimentally eliminated from the animal's use by destruction of sense organs or by removing stimuli, the worse its performance, regardless of which particular sensory cues are eliminated. Since the rat's cortex is primarily a sensory cortex, it is reasonable to believe that the larger the cortical lesion, the more it will impair the use of sensory cues and, therefore, the poorer will be the maze performance. Arguing somewhat against this interpretation is an ingenious experiment that Lashley performed. He taught blind rats a maze and then removed the visual cortex. Because they showed defects in the retention of the maze habit, he concluded that the visual cortex had nonvisual functions in learning and memory as well as visual functions.

Many learning experiments of this type, involving various sensory capacities, have been done on different mammals, and the results have in general been the same. The cortex, then, is not essential for learning or memory. The defects seen after cortical lesions are largely a matter of the sensory defects produced. One exception to this general statement is the recent work exploring the temporal cortex of primates. Work with monkeys shows that there are defects in learning touch discriminations following lesions of the posterior borders of the temporal lobe and defects in learning visual discriminations after lesions somewhat more anterior in the temporal lobe. Also, it has been found that human patients with bilateral temporal cortex damage seem to have defects of memory, especially recent memory, as we shall see at the end of this chapter. Finally, a most interesting related finding is that electrical stimulation of the temporal cortex of fully awake epileptic patients evokes past memories in a vivid dream-like sequence. This, however, may possibly arise as much from arousal of subcortical structures as from the effect on the cortex itself.

Efforts to use the lesion method to explore the role of subcortical structures in learning have not been highly fruitful as yet. Not many such experiments have been done, and what information we have has been largely negative. Two recent studies, however, have provided hopeful leads. In one, the experimenters tried to condition brain-wave responses after making irritative lesions on one side of the brain by implanting aluminum cream. Of all the loci they investigated, placement of the irritative focus just below the temporal cortex in the amygdala and hippocampus was the most effective in impairing learning. In the second experiment, monkeys were required to discriminate whether two patterns of tone or of light were the same or different, even though the two patterns might be separated in time by several seconds. In this case, surgical lesion of the region of the amygdala and hippocampus turned out to produce the most marked defects. Such operated monkeys could tell that the two patterns were the same only if one followed immediately after the other. It was as though the lesion made them unable to remember the first pattern over time, for they failed the test when the two patterns were separated by a few seconds.

Another approach to the understanding of brain mechanisms involved in learning is through the use of electrical recording methods in which it is possible to trace changes in the electrical activity of many parts of the brain during learning. In these experiments, an animal has electrodes chronically implanted in its brain, and changes in patterns of electrical activity are noted as the animal is trained. The striking thing here is that the changes take place in many parts of the brain, cortically and subcortically, within the sensory systems and outside of them as well. It may be that the electrical method is so sensitive in recording changes that go on in learning that it cannot separate the important from the unimportant parts of the brain for learning and memory. Or it may be that learning, or different facets of learning, occur in many places of the brain at once, and that therefore no one part is completely essential for its formation or retention.

When we come to the second question, concerning *the nature of the change in learning,* we find mostly theories and very little facts. Various mechanisms have been suggested as being responsible for the establishment of new functional connections in the nervous system: (1) the growth of new nerve pathways, (2) anatomical swelling or sprouting of synaptic terminals, resulting in the facilitation of crossing certain synapses, (3) a physiological increase in the ease of crossing synaptic connections already established but not functional at the start of training, and (4) biochemical changes such as alterations in the structural arrangement of protein molecules in nerve cells. Of all these suggestions, one of the most intriguing has been the physiological concept of a recurrent nerve circuit in which a loop or circle of connecting neurons is activated in such a way that each neuron in the circle activates the next until the first one, having time to recover, is activated again. Such a loop could theoretically continue firing indefinitely and serve to add facilitation to any synapses it makes outside the loop and thus provide the basis for long-term memory. Although it is known that such loops exist in the nervous system, unfortunately there is no direct evidence that they function in learning and memory.

An even more exciting and more daring concept is the biochemical possibility that the memory of a learning experience is encoded in a macromolecule much in the manner that genetic information is believed to be encoded in DNA (deoxyribose nucleic acid). According to this idea, learning causes a modification in the structure of RNA (ribose nucleic acid) so that in its function as a template for the synthesis of proteins, it produces some specific modification of protein structure in nerve cells. The theory is quite speculative, but it has led to some interesting experiments. One, using planaria, concludes that tail sections of trained worms, allowed to regenerate in water containing an enzyme that destroys RNA, fail to retain previous conditioning as tail sections regenerated in plain water do. Another reports that a drug, 8-azaguanine, that inactivates RNA slows the learning of rats. Unfortunately in both experiments, the effects are rather small and neither is sufficiently well controlled.

Far clearer are the results of a study in which protein synthesis, in the brains of mice, was inhibited by the injection of a drug called puromycin. When the drug was injected into the posterior region of the brain after the learning of a simple position habit in a Y-maze, there was complete loss of memory two days old or less, but no effect on memory six days old. To eliminate such longer-term memory, it was necessary to affect most of the rest of the cerebral cortex with puromycin at the same time. Much remains to be learned before our knowledge of the memory trace is on firm ground, but significant new possibilities have been opened up by the biochemical approach.

Some further insight into the nature of memory mechanisms has been gained by direct, experimental examination of *temporal characteristics of the memory process*. In one study, rats were trained to run from one compartment to another to avoid an electric shock. They were given one trial a day, and after each trial, they received an electroconvulsive shock through the head. Different groups of rats received the convulsive shock at different times after the learning trial: after 20 sec, 1 min, 4 min, 15 min, 1 hr, 4 hr, and 14 hr. If the shock came within an hour, there was virtually no learning, but if it came after four hours, learning was essentially normal. Apparently, memory takes time to "set" in the brain, and this consolidation requires at least an hour, which suggests that memory is a two-part process, consisting of an early phase when memory is vulnerable to convulsive shock and a later phase when it is not.

The same kind of conclusion turns up in two other rather different studies. In one, an octopus was trained, as we mentioned earlier, to discriminate between a crab it could eat and a crab, accompanied by a white card, that it could not approach under penalty of electric shock. If the octopus' vertical lobe, an associational region of the brain, was removed, then a curious thing happened. When the trials were spaced more than an hour apart, the animal could not retain enough from trial to trial to improve its performance in normal fashion. When the trials were within fifteen minutes of each other, however, it was able to learn easily. Apparently, lesion of the vertical lobe affected the "permanent" laying down of memories, but did not disturb their "temporary" establishment.

In man, lesions of the temporal cortex on both sides of the brain may result in a similar defect. Patients with this affliction can learn something simple and retain it for about fifteen minutes to an hour, but after that time, they forget completely and may not even remember having learned. Yet their life-long memories are left undisturbed. Taken together with the animal studies, this finding suggests that memory is a two-part process: (1) an initial, vulnerable, perhaps physiological process lasting fifteen minutes to an hour, and (2) a later, invulnerable, perhaps anatomical process, providing the permanent basis for memory.

Many mysteries remain in our quest for the physiological basis of simple learning. We know that learning is a property of at least all animals with a synaptic nervous system. The major question is whether the superior learning of mammals and especially primates is due to the development of superior neural mechanisms for learning and memory or to their greatly increased sensory and motor capacities or to both. As we shall see in the next chapter, the development of superior neural mechanisms must be an important factor, for the capacities for complex learning, problem solution, and reasoning emerge with the evolution of the central nervous system.

SUMMARY

We have reviewed, in this chapter, the basic facts of animal learning. We began with the concept that learning represents an *enduring modification of behavior* brought about by experience. Then we described various kinds of learning from the simple to the complex: habituation, classical conditioning, instrumental conditioning, and trial-and-error learning. The essential modification in behavior in all these cases is the development of some new response to a stimulus that never before elicited that response. As to the critical elements of the experience in learning, they appear to be very much the same in all these cases. Or put another way, these various instances of learning, including human verbal learning, all seem to obey the same fundamental laws of learning: contiguity, repetition, reinforcement, and, for the case of extinction or forgetting, interference.

When we took up the *phylogenetic development of learning,* we could not find clear-cut and reliable evidence for learning until the level of the worms. This is the point in phylogeny where the bilaterally symmetrical, synaptic nervous system first appears. With the cephalopods and arthropods, which have relatively large, concentrated ganglionic masses in the anterior regions of the nervous system, learning ability is much greater than in the worms. Finally, with the development of the vertebrate brain, learning capacity develops even further, gradually reaching an asymptote among the simpler mammals (see Fig. 6-1).

Despite this evidence that relates learning ability to the development of the central nervous system in phylogeny, it has not been easy to discover, with any degree of specificity, the neural basis of learning. The evidence from experimental brain lesions and, more particularly, from studies that record changes in the electrical activity of the brain during learning suggests that learning takes place in many places within the brain at once. The nature of the neural change in learning has proven elusive, however, despite the many attractive and plausible theories that have been proposed. At present, we know that learning or, more particularly, the formation of memories is at least a two-part process. Initially, there is a temporary, perhaps physiological process, lasting up to an hour in the mammalian nervous system. Following this and perhaps as a result of it, there is a second, more permanent, perhaps biochemical or anatomical change. Still a third mechanism may subserve the storage of longstanding memories, for it is possible to impair the permanent laying down of new memories by brain lesions without impairing either old, longstanding memories or the temporary acquisition of new ones.

Complex
Processes

CHAPTER EIGHT

We have now discussed the evolution of basic behavioral capacities in the animal kingdom. We began with the *basic sensory, motor,* and *associational capacities* that developed as properties of the nervous system and its associated sense organs and muscles. These make up the biological machinery for an organism's selective sensitivity to its environment, for its ability to respond to stimulation, and for the organization of its responses into integrated action. Next we took up the *stereotyped behaviors,* the taxes, reflexes, and instincts that constitute the inborn adaptive mechanisms with which an organism faces the world. Finally, we discussed *learning,* the capacity of an organism to modify its behavior in the light of its individual experience.

As organisms evolved from simple irritable protoplasm to multicellular animals containing more and more complex nervous systems, behavior changed from a simple diffusely and crudely responsive mechanism to one that was capable of increasingly discrete and refined responses, organized into more and more complex, adaptive behaviors, which eventually became modifiable according to the adaptive requirements of an individual's life history. Gradually, in evolution, each new capacity emerged, first as an increase in the refinement and complexity of behavior, eventually as new kinds of adaptive capacities. As we pointed out earlier, at each stage of phylogeny, the new modes of adaptation became the dominant modes until finally, in man, we see reasoning, symbolic capacity, and social organization as the dominant modes of coping with the environment. Gradually, these capacities must have emerged in the subhuman forms, and we should be able to trace them in the study of lower animals as rudimentary, emerging capacities.

REASONING

Let us look first at *reasoning* capacity, the ability to solve complex problems with something more than simple trial-and-error, habit, or stimulus-response modifications. In man, we recognize this capacity as the ability to develop concepts, to behave according to general principles, and to put together elements from past experience into a new organization, quite independently of the particular physical form a problem takes or the specific sensory or motor elements involved in the situation. What do we observe in animals? In the last chapter, we described many cases of complex learning in which an organism was required to handle many stimuli at once and to make a complex sequence of discriminative responses. Now we want to see performance in situations where specific sensory cues and specific habits are not critical for the solution of a problem.

A number of techniques have been devised to investigate such problem-solution capacities in animals, and these have met with varying degrees of success. One of the oldest, and in some ways the simplest, of these techniques is the *detour problem* (Fig. 8-1). Here an animal is blocked from direct approach to food he can see and smell by a barrier or some other arrangement. To get the food, the animal must first move away from it and thus make a "detour" from the direct path. Several questions are pertinent. Can the animal solve the problem on its first exposure to it, that is, without having to learn by trial and error? Can an animal eventually learn to solve the problem? Or does it fail or simply have occasional "accidental" solutions as a result of excited running about? Of all the animals tested in detour problems, only monkeys and chimpanzees show any degree of success upon first exposure to the situation. Many other animals have learned to perform detours after failing on their first few trials. The octopus, for instance, can slowly learn to detour under some conditions, but not others. Fish and birds eventually learn the long way around a barrier. Laboratory-reared rats, dogs, and raccoons are rapid learners, although they initially fail.

Making a detour on first exposure is similar to what we call *insight* into a problem in man. Even more direct evidence for insight-type solutions can be seen in other kinds of experiments with chimpanzees and, to some de-

Fig. 8-1. A detour problem for the raccoon in which the animal must first go away from the bait in order to reach it. (Redrawn from Maier and Schneirla.)

Bait

Fig. 8-2. A chimpanzee solves the problem of getting a banana that is out of reach by stacking boxes on top of one another. (From Maier and Schneirla.)

gree, with monkeys. These studies, first performed by Wolfgang Köhler during World War I, showed, for example, that a chimpanzee is capable of attaining a banana out of reach by stacking boxes beneath it and climbing up (Fig. 8-2). Or a chimpanzee will fit two sticks together to pull in a piece of food that is out of reach of either stick alone. Unfortunately, it is difficult to be certain in these cases that the animal did not have some experience with a similar type of problem before. Even so, the immediate application of past experience in a new situation is a noteworthy capacity.

To test for the application of past experiences to the solution of a new problem in a rat, the animal is taught two elements necessary for the solution of a problem and then observed to see if it can combine them satisfactorily. For example, the rat is taught to climb down from a table to the floor where it can explore the room (Fig. 8-3). This is the first element. The second element is to train the animal to climb up another table and cross a runway to find food on a corner of the first table that is fenced off from the rest of it. When this is learned, the animal is placed on the first table on the opposite side of the fence from the food. Once it has mastered the two separate elements, the rat is able to climb down from the first table, run across the floor to the second table, climb it, and reach the food behind the fence. This, of course, is a detour problem in which the animal is trained in the elements of the solution beforehand and is required to put them together for the first time when the test is made.

Other approaches to the ability to solve problems in the animal kingdom have required animals to learn to perform a task according to some general principle, quite aside from the specific stimuli available at the time the response is made. These animals are given a great deal of training. The major question is whether they can learn to master the problem at all. If they do learn, there is the question of how rapidly they can master it and at what level of complexity they can perform. One of the easiest of these problems is the *conditional reaction*. In this case, an animal might have to learn to choose the left of two gray doors if it is preceded by a single black door or the right door if it is preceded by a single white door; or to choose a door with the triangle instead of a door with the circle if the background has horizontal black and white stripes and the one with the circle instead of the one with the triangle if the stripes are vertical. This is an "if—then reaction"; if the stripes are horizontal, then the door with the triangle is correct. Rats can gradually learn this type of response when asked to make appropriate left-right choices in a long runway divided alternately by single-cue doors (black or white) and double-choice doors (gray). Monkeys learn conditional reactions more readily, and are more versatile and stable in their solutions.

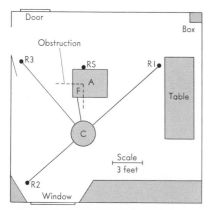

Fig. 8-3. The problem for the rat is to get from Table A to food at F when an obstruction blocks its way. First the rat is trained to go from A to the floor by way of a ladder down a ringstand, RS. Later it is trained to climb from the floor up ringstands R1, R2, or R3 and to reach Table C over the runways. From C it can get to F over a runway. The test is to see if the rat can combine two separate experiences and go directly from A to the floor to C to F on the first test. (Redrawn from Maier and Schneirla.)

A more difficult type of principle-learning is what Harry F. Harlow has called the *learning set* (Fig. 8-4). Here an animal is first required to discriminate two common objects (e.g., a white jar lid and a red pincushion) that differ from each other in a number of physical dimensions. Displacement of the correct object, regardless of its position, yields food to the hungry subject. A monkey, for example, may require 50–100 trials to master such a problem. After this, other different pairs of objects are presented for discrimination training. When a number of these have been learned, each

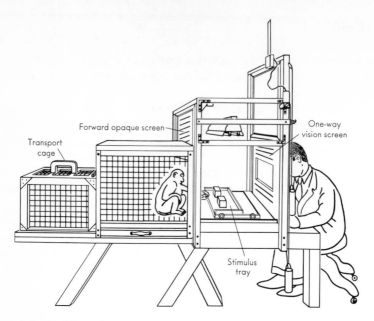

Fig. 8-4. The Wisconsin General Testing Apparatus for testing discrimination, learning set, and the solution of related problems in the rhesus monkey. (From Stone.)

succeeding new pair of objects is presented for only five or six trials. After 200–300 such 6-trial presentations, the monkey can learn to make each new discrimination in one or two trials.

By chance, it can get the first trial correct only half the time. When it "guesses" correctly on the first trial, then it will choose correctly in the remaining five trials and ignore the incorrect object. When it "guesses" incorrectly, it typically shifts to the other object and never goes back to the incorrect one. Thus, the first trial is an "information" trial upon which succeeding choices are based, as though in accordance with the principle: "If the first choice is correct, continue to choose that object and ignore the other; if it is incorrect, never go back to it." In essence, the animal has been trained to the point of "one-trial" learning, and this is similar to the insight case. Only primates have any degree of success in this type of problem. Rats fail miserably and must learn each new problem by trial and error, never carrying over the general principle from problem to problem.

Very similar but even more difficult is *oddity-principle learning,* in which three objects are presented, two the same and one different (Fig. 8-5). The task is to pick the one different object, the odd one. Monkeys can master this task to the point where they are correct on the first trial of a new trio of objects on most occasions. Again, rats must learn each task anew and never reach the point where they succeed on the first trial.

Still another type of problem is the *delayed reaction,* in which a hungry animal is presented with two identical cups. It is allowed to see food

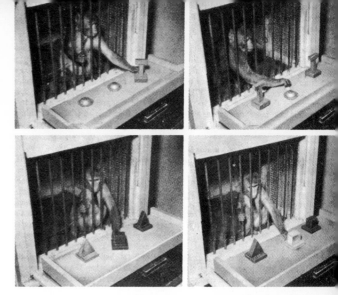

Fig. 8-5. A rhesus monkey performing an oddity-principle test. (From Stone.)

placed under one cup and then, after some delay, is released to make its choice by displacing one cup. With odor controlled, the animal has no discriminative cue at the time of choice between two identical cups other than its memory of which one was baited. To be used effectively, this memory must be carried over the period of delay, and it has been suggested that to do this the animal must be capable of some "symbolic process," akin to language, which it can use to represent the missing discriminative cue at the time of choice. Animals like the rat, cat, and dog solve this problem by orienting toward the baited cup during the delay and then "following their noses" to the correct cup. If they break orientation during the delay, or if the experimenter disorients them, they fail. Thus, they do not seem to show evidence of symbolic capacity. Raccoons, interestingly enough, are capable of short delays without orientation. Primates, however, are capable of much longer delays than rodents and carnivores and, what is more important, do not maintain an orientation toward the correct stimulus during the delay period. They may even be removed from the test situation and returned after the delay and still perform successfully.

Another kind of symbolic process, akin to counting, is thought to be involved in the *double-alternation test*. Again, a hungry animal is presented with two identical stimuli covering food wells, but this time the correct one is given simply by the order RRLL; that is, the food appears twice on the right and twice on the left, and it is this sequence that the animal must master. Rats fail this test. Cats will master a simple RRLL sequence with prolonged training, but they cannot extend the series; raccoons have been able to extend it as far as RRLLRR. Subhuman primates have extended the series to RRLLRRLL, but it is not until we get to man that indefinite extension of the series is possible.

Even more complex and more arbitrary sequences may be required of

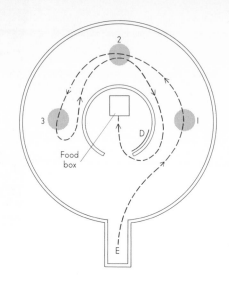

Fig. 8-6. The triple-plate problem requires an animal to push one or all of three plates (1, 2, 3) in some sequence to open the food box. This test is a good one to compare the ability of different mammals to learn sequences because, first, the task of pushing plates is just about equally simple for all mammals and, second, the sequences can be arranged from the very simple to the very complex. The sequence here is difficult, requiring the animal to push plates 1, 2, 3, and 2, in that order, before going to the food box. D indicates door to food; E, entrance. (Redrawn from N. L. Munn, The Evolution and Growth of Human Behavior. **Boston: Houghton Mifflin, 1955.)**

animals in the *triple-plate problem* (Fig. 8-6). Here the animal simply has to press three pedals in some predetermined order, including the possibility that some pedals might have to be pressed more than once, not necessarily in succession. Pressing the correct sequence of pedals automatically opens a door to food. This test has been successfully used with guinea pigs, rats, kittens, and rhesus and cebus monkeys. Guinea pigs and rats are capable of pressing up to two or three pedals in order; kittens can handle as high as a sequence of seven; monkeys, sequences of fifteen to twenty.

BRAIN FUNCTION IN PROBLEM SOLUTION

Given these tests of problem solution involving insight, reasoning, concept formation, principle-learning, and symbolic processes, we are now faced with the question about what parts of the brain might be critically involved. Because performance on these tests improves so dramatically with the higher animals and, indeed, is sometimes possible only in the primates, the more recently evolved parts of the brain—the cerebral cortex and particularly its association areas—must be involved. This appears to be the case in the delayed-reaction test, where brain function has been extensively studied; lesions of the cortex of the frontal lobe render the monkey incapable of handling delays of more than a few seconds.

It is still not safe, however, to conclude that the frontal lobes are essential for either recent memory or the symbolic processes believed to be required in delayed action. The situation is just too complex. The monkey without its frontal lobes has difficulty maintaining attention, for it is hyperactive and easily distracted by any visual stimuli. Two experiments have shown that the monkey without its frontal lobes can perform the delayed-reaction test if its ability to be distracted is counteracted. In one, the operated animal's attention to the baiting of the correct cup was improved by simply feeding it at the correct cup before the delay. In the other, the animal was plunged into darkness during the delay period, and this served to keep it very quiet. So we cannot say that the monkey without its frontal lobes has lost recent memory or the symbolic capacity required for delayed reaction. Obviously, it is simply too inattentive and distractible to perform well.

Some evidence in animal experiments suggests that the associational area in the temporal lobe is important in the development of learning sets and that the visual associational area in the occipital lobe is required for problems involving visual recognition of objects. The evidence is neither extensive nor conclusive, however.

Not until we get to studies of *brain injury in man* can we gain any real appreciation of brain function in complex intellectual processes. This is partly because animal experiments have not progressed far enough in investigating brain function in reasoning and partly because only man has reasoning processes, and especially symbolic processes, that are developed far enough to provide a good basis for study.

The literature on brain injury in man is voluminous, but we shall only be able to cover some of the highlights, with emphasis on those that are pertinent to problems raised in the study of animals. Many studies indicate that intellectual deficit may follow lesions of the frontal lobe. This is clearly seen in cases of psychosurgery where bilateral damage is done to the frontal lobes in order to control insanity or intractible pain and where the surgical damage tends to be somewhat back from the tips of the frontal lobes. Although the intellectual impairment may show itself in many ways, including inability to perform the double alternation test, it can generally be characterized as a loss of abstract as opposed to concrete ability. For example, the frontal patient may be unable to "make believe" he is drinking from an empty glass or to go through the motions of writing his name with imaginary chalk on an imaginary blackboard. He is unable to carry out an idea in the abstract. If water is put in the glass, however, or if he is given chalk and a blackboard, he can follow the instructions normally, showing that he has the requisite abilities in the concrete situation.

When the brain injury is in the visual associational area, the patient may have a visual *agnosia,* which is inability to recognize common objects visually although he can see quite well and can recognize the objects through other senses. With parietal lobe injury, the agnosia may be tactual as well as visual, even to the point where the individual may not be able to recognize part of his body, such as his hand, as his own. In some cases, the defect is on the motor side (*apraxia*), and the patient is unable to carry out a meaningful movement like hammering a nail, even though his motor reflexes are quite normal.

Perhaps the most striking of all the effects of brain injury in man are the *aphasias,* or language disorders. These take different forms depending on the region of damage. If the damage is anterior in the cortex, the result will be a motor disorder such as the inability to name objects upon request; this result is seen after damage to Broca's area at the bottom of the motor cortex. Or it may take the form of an agraphia, an inability to respond in writing. More posterior lesions result in sensory aphasias—either auditory, in which there is impaired comprehension of the spoken word, or visual, with impaired comprehension of the written word (alexia). In all these cases, the individual's sensory and motor capacity may be quite normal, and his general comprehension may be good, but he simply blocks and gropes unsuccessfully, much as the normal person does when he cannot think of someone's name.

Much is yet to be learned about reasoning and symbolic capacity and their neural mechanisms in man, and, as we have pointed out, our knowledge of animals is even more deficient. But what we have learned so far shows that there is continuity from animal to man, even though man's specialization is so great that the step from animal to man is an enormously large one. Although only the mere rudiments of reasoning and symbolic processes are observed in animals, these processes are definitely there, and in animals such as the subhuman primates, they contribute to behavior in a way that clearly marks them off from the subprimate animals. So, although it is dangerous to overestimate the ability of animals by attributing human capacities to them, it is also dangerous to underestimate animals, especially the primates, and try to account for their behavior solely in terms of simple stimulus-response associations.

Our conclusion, then, is that with the great development of the cortex in the subhuman primates and man, particularly of its association areas and related thalamic nuclei, new capacities for behavior emerge in evolution that fall under the general category of reasoning, abstract ability, and symbolic process. When these are developed, an organism is freed from slavish dependence on sensory stimuli, instinct, or habit and can make its adaptations to the environment with insight, reasoning, and the use of symbols, and ultimately of language.

SOCIAL ORGANIZATION

One notable consequence of the development of these higher processes is the possibility of a social organization that provides a cultural heritage upon which man's adaptation to his environment can be progressively (and hopefully) improved. When we look back over the animal kingdom and examine the precursors of social behavior, we find there have been two types of social organization in evolution: one in the invertebrates and simpler vertebrates based on instinct, and one in man and the subhuman primates based on reasoning and symbolic capacities.

Social behavior, by definition, implies the interaction of two or more individuals, the influence of one individual on another. The mere existence of group behavior, however, does not guarantee social behavior. For example, the orientation and movement of a group of paramecia toward a source of light is simply an aggregation of individuals responding to a common external stimulus. So are the circling of a group of moths around a lamp and the feeding of flies on a lump of sugar. Each individual would respond in the same way even if alone.

In at least one respect—in reproductive behavior—almost all multicellular animals are social. The grayling butterfly shows no social behavior in its life cycle until it is time to mate. Then it begins an elaborate courtship. The male stops foraging and waits alertly for the female. Each time a female passes, the male flies in pursuit. If she alights and remains motionless, he jerks his wings and opens and closes them, exposing their spots. Then he does a deep bow, walks around her and brings his abdomen in contact with her copulatory organs. Here social behavior stops; the male never interacts with others again, and the female lays her eggs on food objects in the grass and leaves them.

An even more elaborate pattern in the stickleback fish was described (p. 71), in which the male builds a nest, fights off intruding males, entices a female into the nest, induces her to lay eggs, fertilizes the eggs, cares for them by fanning them, and guards the young for a period of time after hatching. In birds like the herring gull, pairs remain together for longer periods, establish a territory, cooperate in building a nest, and go through patterns of courtship and copulation repeatedly. The male fights and threatens other males with highly specific postures, gestures, and calls. When the eggs are laid, the male and female take turns incubating them, one releasing the other with a highly specific approach to the nest. After the young are hatched, the cooperation extends to feeding and guarding them. When predators enter the colony, the adults sound the alarm call and fly up, and the chicks run for cover. The birds then swoop down upon the intruders and "bomb" them with regurgitated food and feces.

As we saw earlier, these interactions among individuals are largely innate patterns, which are heavily dependent on hormones and are released by highly specific "sign stimuli" provided by another individual. Sometimes the releasing stimulus is a morphological change induced by hormones, such as the brilliant coloration of the male stickleback. Sometimes it is a behavorial response such as the bow of the grayling. Typically, the sign stimulus and the response to it are parts of a complex chain such as the alarm reaction to an intruder, which produces a warning call, which in turn releases flight in individuals who have not been stimulated by the intruder.

To some degree the effectiveness of a sign stimulus may depend on learning, as in the case of imprinting where the innate filial following response is specifically released by the individual or object present at the time of hatching. Or in an even more complicated instance, the reproductive behavior of the female ring-dove is instigated by the sight of the male, which sets off hormonal reactions in her, which are important in setting the stage for mating, nestbuilding, and incubating eggs. To a large degree, the effectiveness of the male, the nest, and the eggs as stimuli depends on the past experience of the female. As we shall see in a moment, learning figures even more prominently in the social behavior of mammals, especially primates. This is not to say, however, that the innate, releasing sign stimulus is not a basic mechanism in the organization of social behavior. Even in man we see evidence of its effects in the spread of emotion in a mob, where emotional reactions in an individual may be triggered by emotional expressions and gestures in others.

On the basis of innate patterns, remarkable social organizations have developed, perhaps reaching their peak in insects. Ants have wondrously complex social organizations which contain specialized classes of individuals and in which cultivation of fungus "gardens," "milking" of aphids, and exclusion of outsiders to the colony may be seen. Bees are even more complex, for in addition to their morphologically specialized classes of individuals and intricate hive organization, they communicate information about the location of food sources through the waggle dance, a phenomenon called the "language of the bees" by the eminent German biologist von Frisch. Upon returning from a food source, a bee performs the dance on the vertical surface of the combs of the hive (Fig. 8-7); the dance takes the form of a figure 8 in which the bee "waggles" its abdomen in a straight path across the middle of the 8. Other bees in the hive follow the movements of the dancer to obtain the distance and direction of the food. The distance is given by the rate of dancing, with the number of dances per unit of time decreasing as the distance to the food increases. The direction is given in relation to the position of the sun, so that a dance that has the waggle going up indicates food is in the direction of the sun and a dance with a waggle down shows food in the opposite direction; the direction to the right and left of the sun are given by having the waggle to the right or left. Upon completion of the dance, the bees leave the hive and go directly to the food.

Fig. 8-7. The "waggle dance" of the bee, showing the sequence of movements (1–8) that gives it the form of a figure 8.

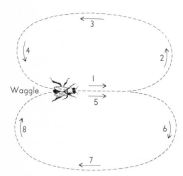

Although fish, birds, and subprimate mammals show some social behavior in migration, reproductive activities, territorial defense, fighting, and particularly in schooling, flocking, and herding, they have little of the complex organization of insects. Some birds diplay a pecking order in which the dominant bird pecks the more submissive bird. Chickens show "social facilitation" so that when a bird has fed to repletion, it feeds again if another hungry bird is introduced. Many mammals have a dominance hierarchy similar to the pecking order of birds. In one study of a group of rats kept in a large outdoor pen, it was found that the larger, more vigorous rats lived near the central supply of food and dominated all the others. The oldest rats lived out on the perimeter and fed only during the day. Submissive young rats lived in between and apparently became submissive through defeats in fighting to the point where they turned and ran even at the approach of a dominant rat. Most interesting of all, when the young of submissive rats left their nests and wandered into the territory of dominant rats, the dominant females would seize them and "drub" them with their paws without inflicting injury. After a few such treatments, the offspring of submissive rats became submissive.

Such mechanisms for the development of dominance and submissiveness also have importance for the physiology of organisms, the health of individuals, and the size of populations. As population grows and the pressure that dominant animals put on the submissive ones increases, various endocrine changes take place, particularly enlargements and exhaustion of the adrenals and regression of the gonads of the submissive animals. The result is infertility and increased susceptibility to disease, not only infectious ones, but also cardiovascular, pancreatic, etc. Thus there is an inevitable decline in the population. This sequence of events has been observed in chickens and mice in the laboratory, woodchucks and deer in the wild, and is believed to be a major factor in many of the degenerative diseases of civilization in man.

Obviously, learning plays an important role in many instances of vertebrate social organization. The following of the mother by ducklings through the process of imprinting is a good example of this. In still another example, the herding of sheep, early experiences like imprinting are required, for if a lamb is raised by man for even a short time after birth, it fails to follow the herd normally and may be rejected by its mother.

Among the subhuman primates, social organization is more complex again, and this time it is apparently dependent on learning and higher processes. Monkeys, for example, will organize in bands around a large male "chief" who is the dominant member of the group and who has a "harem" of females. The chief commands until challenged and defeated by another male. Then he, along with other old males, may be ostracized from the group and forced to live alone. The vocal communication of monkeys is limited to food cries and warning cries. For example, "sentinels" give warning cries when another group of monkeys invades their territory. The females and young retreat to the rear, and the chief and young males advance to meet the intruders.

The subhuman primate, nevertheless, is severely limited in its social behavior and communicative powers. Occasional hand-reared chimpanzees have been laboriously taught to use one or two words with some slight degree of success. In the laboratory, two chimpanzees can be trained to work together to pull in food on a weighted board that is too heavy for either one of them, and they will call and gesture to one another to enlist aid. In food competition, a female chimpanzee will present herself sexually to a male and, as he begins to mount, snatch the food and run off. But remarkable as they may be, these are relatively simple instances of social behavior, and it is not until the full development of language and reasoning in man that truly complex social organization again becomes possible in the animal kingdom. We see once more that although there is evolutionary continuity in the development of social organization, the advance from animal to man is tremendous.

SUMMARY

In this chapter, we have described the emergence of reasoning and the symbolic process in phylogeny. With the development of the associational areas of the cerebral cortex, the organism becomes free of strict stimulus control of its behavior. It is no longer a simple creature of instinct and habit, but is capable of insight, the formation of concepts and principles, and the use of symbolic processes in the solution of problems. Compared to man, animals possess only rudimentary powers of reasoning and symbolic behavior, and, to a large degree, such behavior does not appear until the development of the primates.

One product of the evolution of symbolic processes and reasoning is the development of the capacity for complex social organization, which is observed so clearly in man. Such social behavior is in contrast to the highly specialized and innately determined social organization seen in the invertebrates and most highly developed in the insects. The lower vertebrates, including simple mammals, show only rudimentary capabilities for social organization. Some increase in social behavior appears in the subhuman primates, but even so, the step from animal to man is a giant one.

SELECTED READINGS

Adrian, E. D., *The Physical Background of Perception*. London: Clarendon Press, 1947. A brief account, by one of the pioneers of modern electrophysiology, of the electrical activity of nerve cells and the ways in which this activity is coded to provide the basis of sensation and perception.

Brazier, M. A. B., *The Electrical Activity of the Nervous System*. London: Pitman, 1951. A concise modern treatment of electrical activity in the nervous system that will serve as a good introduction to this field.

von Frisch, K., *The Dancing Bees*. London: Methuen, 1954. A fascinating monograph, by the man who did the original investigations, describing the way in which bees communicate the location of food to others in the hive; includes an account of the sensory capacities required in locating food, the "waggle dance" that communicates information, and the navigational abilities used by new individuals in finding food.

Lenhoff, H. M., and W. F. Loomis, *The Biology of Hydra*. Miami, Florida: Univ. Miami Press, 1961. A collection of reports by different workers recounting the latest advances in research with Hydra.

Lorenz, K. Z., *King Solomon's Ring: New Light on Animal Ways*. New York: Crowell, 1952. A popular book by the founder of modern ethology describing the way in which careful field and laboratory observations permit the uncovering and understanding of many remarkable examples of animal behavior.

Maier, N. R. F., and T. C. Schneirla, *Principles of Animal Psychology*. New York: McGraw-Hill, 1935. A classical textbook of comparative psychology, systematically covering the animal kingdom from protozoa to primates.

Morgan, C. T., and E. Stellar, *Physiological Psychology*. New York: McGraw-Hill, 1950. A standard textbook of physiological psychology describing physiological mechanisms underlying behavior.

Parker, G. H., *The Elementary Nervous System*. Philadelphia: Lippincott, 1919. A classical and highly readable account of the evolution of the structure and function of the nervous systems of the lower animals.

Romer, A. S., *The Vertebrate Body*. Philadelphia: Saunders, 1955. One of the best treatments of comparative anatomy, with an excellent chapter on the vertebrate nervous system.

Scott, J. P., *Animal Behavior*. Chicago: University of Chicago Press, 1958. A treatment of vertebrate behavior with special emphasis on learning and particularly early life experience in the genesis of social behavior.

———, *Aggression*. Chicago: University of Chicago Press, 1958. An examination of the psychological, physiological, social, and ecological bases of aggression.

Stone, K. P., ed., *Comparative Psychology.* Englewood Cliffs, N. J.: Prentice-Hall, 1951. A collection of chapters by various authorities in the field of animal behavior organized around current topics in experimental psychology.

Tartar, V., *The Biology of Stentor.* London, England: Pergamon Press, 1961. An excellent resume of our knowledge of an interesting protozoan.

Thorpe, W. H., *Learning and Instinct in Animals.* Cambridge: Harvard University Press, 1956. An attempt to synthesize the approaches to the study of animal behavior used by ethologists and psychologists; special attention is devoted to insects and birds.

————, and O. L. Zangwill, eds., *Current Problems in Animal Behaviour.* Cambridge, England: Cambridge University Press, 1961. A series of essays on current problems in animal behavior by a group of Cambridge scientists.

Tinbergen, N., *The Study of Instinct.* Oxford, England: Clarendon Press, 1951. A classical statement of the original position of European ethologists; provides valuable insight into the ethological method of approach.

————, *Social Behaviour in Animals.* London, England: Methuen, 1953. A classical account of patterns of social behavior in the animal kingdom.

Waters, R. H., D. A. Rethlingshafer, and W. E. Caldwell, *Principles of Comparative Psychology.* New York: McGraw-Hill, 1960. A modern textbook written from the point of view of American psychology with strong emphasis on learning.

Wells, M. J., *Brain and Behaviour in Cephalopods.* Stanford: Stanford University Press, 1962. A complete account of behavior studies with special emphasis on learning and its neurological correlates.

Index

113